EXPERIMENTS

This book is now
published by
CHATTO & WINDUS
40-42 William IV Street
London, W.C. 2

EXPERIMENTS

BY
NORMAN DOUGLAS

Author of
"Southwind," "They Went," "Alone," "Together," etc.

SECOND IMPRESSION

CHAPMAN AND HALL L^D.

LONDON: MCMXXVI

First Published . . . . . *October 1925*
Second Impression . . . . *May 1926*

PRINTED IN GREAT BRITAIN BY
NORTHUMBERLAND PRESS LIMITED, NEWCASTLE-UPON-TYNE

CONTENTS

ARABIA DESERTA

A

Arabia Deserta [1]

NOT long ago there was sent me a recently-
published French book about Morocco
—*Marrakech*, by the brothers Tharaud,
then already in its twenty-fifth edition. What did
I think of it? And why could we not write such
things in English?

Well, I thought it good, despite that unseason-
able military atmosphere—decidedly good of its
kind; the story grows livelier and impressive towards
the end. Moreover, thank Heaven, it exhales but
faintly the familiar odour of Parisian patchouli;
there are some luminous and suggestive metaphors
and a moment of real tragedy. For the rest: head-
work, self-conscious glitter, a virtuosity bordering
on the precious. One detects only the frailest link
of human sympathy between the authors and the
scenes they describe. A wealth of outlandish
customs and figures has been noted down by the pen
of a scrupulous journalist and then distilled into
elaborately-tinted phrases. It is almost wearisome,
all this material, where so much is seen, so little
felt. I recall, for instance, that suffocating chapter

[1] *Arabia Deserta.* By Charles M. Doughty. With an introduction by T. E. Lawrence. New Edition.

3

" La Place Folle." " Qu'il est donc malaisé," say
the authors in one place, " de peindre avec justesse
le charme de l'Orient! A inventorier ces beautés
. . . on a l'air d'un pédagogue." Exactly! An
artist should never "inventorier." Why therefore
this endless cataloguing in *Marrakech?* Why?
Because the authors, as Frenchmen, were unable to
do what they should have done—unable to make
their readers really feel the life they depict. Your
Gaul is a centripetal fellow, a bad nomad. His
affinities with foreign folk are only skin-deep—
æsthetic rather than constitutional. One suspects
that, while gadding abroad, he is pretty frequently
homesick. One knows it. He will tell you so
himself.

As to writing such things in English, the feat
is not impossible. We must try, first and foremost,
to be more logical, to rid ourselves of that
lamentable haziness, of those iridescent flashes of
thought and feeling that can be struck out of a
single word; we must learn, in short, to content
ourselves with a vocabulary such as our neighbours
possess. Cut down to a quarter of its size that
preposterous dictionary of ours, throw on the
scrap-heap all those mellow verbal forms, and
consign the residue into the hands of a conscience-
stricken Academy that shall stereotype the meaning
and prescribe the proper usage of every item—the
thing is done. There will be no more half-tones,
no more interplay of shades. We shall step from

twilight into sunshine. For what is the chief
secret of French precision? Lack of words. To
be sure, their writers are mostly professionals—
gens du métier; they know how to handle those few
words.

That is why, generally speaking, they produce
such mediocre travel books.

The *homme de lettres*, of whatever nationality,
is handicapped in this department; he can never
more attain to a jovial heedlessness of expression.
His schooling militates against it; he knows for
whom he writes; he has learnt to play to the gallery.
The personal note (an impersonal travel-book is a
horror) becomes him ill; there is apt to be something
spectacular and meretricious in the work. This
applies particularly to Frenchmen. Having an
old-established literary tradition of what is good
and bad—how to compass the one and avoid the
other—they shine at objective narrative. When
they write, as they sometimes do, in the first person,
they often fail to ring true; art decays into artifice;
it is as if, accustomed to producing fictional
characters in their tales and romances, they would
now read fictitious characters into themselves. Or
else, as in *Marrakech*, they leave a mere blur so
far as personality is concerned. The ideal author
of travel-books is the inspired, or at least enthusiastic, amateur. One would not take it amiss,
furthermore, were he obsessed by some hobby or
grievance, by idiosyncrasies and prejudices not

common to the rest of us. And it goes without saying that he must be gloriously indifferent to the opinions of his fellow-creatures. Can professionals ever fulfil these conditions? No! They should therefore never attempt to write travel-books.

They have lost their innocence.

It was at a friend's house near a green English village, in the heart of a green English summer long ago—years before the abridged edition of *Arabia Deserta* appeared—that I became acquainted with the original Doughty. And these, you may instantly divine, are the conditions most favourable to an appreciation of his merits. That gaunt Odyssey reads mighty well in comfortable England. Amid verdant fields and streamlets, and opulence for the body, and a sense of immemorial tranquillity, how pleasant it is to conjure up visions of the traveller's marches under the flaming sky and of all his other hazards in a land of hunger and blood and desolation! I opened the first volume not quite at the commencement, and remember taking some little credit to myself (one was younger, in the middle 'nineties) for persisting to read to the last word of the second.

A tough, elemental, masculine performance. *Man muss sich hineinlesen*, as the Germans say. The author himself calls his book " not milk for babes." Far from it! Stuff to be humbly and patiently masticated—an unwelcome occupation to

our democratic age which, among other symptoms
of senility, has lost the use of its teeth and now
draws sustenance, ready chewed and half digested,
pepsinised, out of the daily Press. Open *Arabia
Deserta* where you please, and you find yourself
stumbling among thought-laden periods that might
have been hacked out of Chaos by some demoniac
craftsman in the youth of the world. Strange, none
the less, how that sense of anfracuosity evaporates.
The theme, by subtle alchemy, justifies the style.
Those harsh particles of language—so it seemed to
me—were wondrously adapted to mirror the crude-
ness of Arabian landscape and character.

Be that as it may, I felt, on closing the book, as
one who has been forcefully led through all the
harassments of a dream—a weary, lingering dream;
one of those that refuse to relax their hold upon
the imagination, haunting our daylight moments
with a vague presentiment of danger and disquietude.
Here is no glint of mirth, no mockery; a spirit of
sombre truthfulness broods over the scene. The
book is oppressive by weight of thought and length
of text. That might well be appropriate from an
artistic point of view. Nothing short of eleven
hundred pages could do justice to this toilsome,
nightmarish epic. "I passed this one good day in
Arabia; and all the others were evil because of the
people's fanaticism." One good day in two years!
Nor is it a featureless monster, like Pallas' Russian
travels. A well-jointed monster, on the contrary,

of spiky carapace and deliberate gait—pensively alert, harmonious.

Of one thing I was soon convinced: Doughty's outlook was not mine. Never could I have attained to his infinite capacity of suffering fools gladly. My days would have been short among those empty and elvish creatures whose only inducement (as often as not) to offer their far-famed hospitality is that they count on you to feed them another day —which would be almost impossible if they had obeyed their consciences and cut your throat. Dangers of rock or ice or desert may well be tempting, but such fuddled fanaticism grows insupportable. Can there be a greater torture of mind than to travel month after month among peevishly ferocious bigots, repressing an altogether praiseworthy inclination to laugh at them or hit them on the head? In default of being murdered I should have succumbed to cerebral congestion. Doughty's feat calls for quite a peculiar temper:

The mad sherîf had the knife again in his hand! and his old gall rising, " Show me all thou hast," cries he, " and leave nothing; or now will I kill thee."—Where was Maabûb? whom I had not seen since yester-evening; in him was the faintness and ineptitude of Arab friends.— " Remember the bread and salt which we have eaten together, Sâlem! "—" Show it all to me, or now by Ullah I will slay thee with this knife." More bystanders gathered from the shadowing places: some of them cried out, " Let us hack him in morsels, the cursed one! what hinders?—fellows, let us hack him in morsels! "—" Have patience a moment, and send these away." Sâlem, lifting his knife, cried, " Except thou show me all at the instant, I will slay thee! " . . . .

Charming people!

Endeavouring at this distance of time to recall my first impression of *Arabia Deserta*—to delve, that is, through multiple layers of experience which have accumulated since those green summer days of long ago—I remember being vastly pleased with the motives which allured Doughty into these stricken regions. He went not in search of disused emerald mines or to open up commercial markets; he took with him no commission from the home authorities, no theories to air, no gospel to preach. His purport is refreshingly anti-utilitarian. What drove him, besides a Homeric love of adventure, to undergo these hardships was pure intellectual curiosity, the longings of a brain that feeds on disinterested thought. " Other men," said the Arabs to him, " jeopardy somewhat in hope of winning, but thou wilt adventure all, having no need." He hoped, he now tells us, " to add something to the common fund of Western knowledge." A certain Mahmud, describing the rock-hewn sculptures of Medain Salih, " was the father of my painful travels in Arabia." All thanks to Mahmud! Burckhardt's discovery of Petra may have helped to ignite the train; and also the Bible, full as it is of lore and legends of those more reasonable Semites who lived here in olden times, who revered letters and song, and planted the vine, and built cities of stone, before the blight of Islam fell upon the land. That mysterious and romantic background of the past cannot but appeal to the imagination. Doughty's book, so dispassionately worded, is a truthful indictment of Mahomed turning his country into a wilderness. What a creed can do! So Borrow's account of Spanish savagery reflects the achievement of those inquisitors who, in the name of a kindly God, brought to withering-point the kindliness of nature and of man.

And I likewise remember saying to myself, "*Haec olim meminisse* . . . who would not envy this man his memories?"

Ideas such as these will have flitted through the minds of all the early admirers of Doughty. They must have realized that his volumes do provoke thought in no common degree. Here is not only information; here is character, a human document. The image of the poet-traveller is no blur. Doughty has etched his lonely figure against this desolation of sand and lava-crag, and we are glad to see how the thing has been accomplished; it does one good to be in contact with a companion full of natural resources and listen to his tale; one leaves him with regret, as one bids farewell to some friend of robust and well-stored mind, perceiving that, all unconsciously, his words have been of use in revealing us to ourselves. They have helped us to rectify and clarify our own perspective. (Can anything be called a book unless it forces the reader by one method or another, by contrast or sympathy, to discover himself?) So *Arabia Deserta* is the antithesis of the purely pictorial *Marrakech*, inasmuch as therein we enjoy that feeling of intimacy for which every sensitive person must crave, while wandering with his author through strange places. It seems to me that the reader of a good travel-book is entitled not only to an exterior voyage, to descriptions of scenery and so forth, but to an interior, a sentimental or temperamental voyage, which takes place side by side with that outer one; and that the ideal book of this kind offers us, indeed, a triple opportunity of exploration—abroad, into the author's brain, and into our own. The writer should therefore possess a brain worth exploring; some philosophy of life—not necessarily, though by preference, of his own forging—and the courage to proclaim it and put it to the test; he must be naïf and profound, both child and sage. Who is either the one or the other in these days, when the whole trend of existence makes for the superficial and commonplace, when a man writes with one eye on his publisher and the other on his public?

This may account for the insipid taste of many travel-books printed just now: lack of personality on the part of their authors. It is not enough to depict, in however glowing hues, the landscape and customs of distant regions, to smother us in folklore

and statistics and history, and besprinkle the pages
with imaginary conversations or foreign idioms by
way of generating "local colour." It is not
enough. We want to take our share in that interior
voyage and watch how these alien sights and sounds
affect the writer. If he lacks that compulsion of the
spirit which is called character, or lets his mind
linger on contingencies hostile to frank utterance,
he will be unable to supply that want and leave us
dissatisfied. Doughty is rich in character, self-
consistent, never otherwise than himself. Press him
to the last drop, it has the same taste as the first;
whereas Palgrave, for instance, who traversed some
of these same regions, is by no means always
Palgrave; and Burton—what of Burton? A
driving-force void of savour or distinction; drabness
in excelsis; a glorified Blue Book. A man who
could write at one and the same time ten (was it
ten?) different volumes on as many different
subjects. . . .[1]

The modern author of travel-literature one
suspects to be a greyish little person, uncommonly
wide awake, perky and plausible, but somewhat
deficient in humanity—a kind of reporter, in fact,

---

[1] I am far from suggesting that all moderns are drab.
There is, for instance, the *Haji Abdullah Mansur*—Mr. Wyman
Bury—of Aden. Why are those first two volumes of his so
short, especially the second one? What exigencies of time or
space or cost or officialdom were at the back of this mischievous
curtailment? One does not encounter every day a Haji so
brilliant and multi-faceted.

ready to adopt anybody's philosophy or nobody's in particular. Those earlier ones were not of this sort. They derived, to begin with, from another stock, for voyages used to be costly undertakings; they were gentleman-scholars who saw things from their own individual angle. Their leisurely aristocratic flavour, their wholesome discussions about this or that, their waywardness and all that mercurial touch of a bygone generation—where is it now? How went it? An enquiry which, rightly solved, might explain the rarity of types like Doughty.

That mercurial touch disappears naturally when the conditions which gave it birth are at an end. We have ceased to be what we were, that is all. Year by year our hard-won domestic privileges have been gnawed or lopped away; the recent history of the English citizen is one long wail of liberties forfeited; we are being continentalised, standardised—a process which cannot but reflect itself in life and literature. It blunts our peculiar edges. Singularity, the hall-mark of that older Anglo-Saxon, is hardly perceptible in our modern bearing or writing. We have ceased to be " mad "; none but a flatterer would still call us eccentric. All kinds of other factors have contributed to this result, such as improved world-communications. Dr. Arnold, again, that merciless pruner of youthful individualism, has wrought a miracle of destruction so far as originality is concerned, for his energies hit hardest the very class from whom those sturdy and idiomatic, and sometimes outrageous, opinions used to come.

Doughty seems to have escaped the contagion; he goes so far as to call the Universities " shambles of good wits." His edges are intact. He sees clearly, and feels deeply, and warily chooses his words. There is a morning freshness in that gift of investing the ordinary phenomena of life with an extraordinary interest—a kind of bloom, I should call it.

No matins here of birds; not a rock partridge-cock, calling with blithesome chuckle over the extreme waterless desolation. Grave is that giddy heat upon the crown of the head; the ears tingle with a flickering shrillness, a subtle crepitation it seems, in the glassiness of this sun-stricken nature: the hot sand-blink is in the eyes, and there is little refreshment to find in the tents' shelter; the worsted booths leak to this fiery rain of sunny light. Mountains looming like dry bones through the thin air, stand far around about us: the savage flank of Ybba Moghrair, the high spire and ruinous stacks of el-Jebâl, Chebàd, the coast of Helwàn! Herds of weak nomad camels waver dispersedly, seeking pasture in the midst of this hollow fainting country, where but lately the swarming locusts have fretted every green thing. This silent air burning about us, we endure breathless till the assr: when the dozing Arabs in the tents revive after their heavy hours. The lingering day draws down to the sun-setting; the herdsmen, weary of the sun, come again with the cattle, to taste in their menzils the first sweetness of mirth and repose. . . .

Now what do Frenchmen think of such language? And why cannot they convey these shades of meaning in their own?

Well, even Fromentin will give you a taste of that dumb ache which rends and racks the human frame under a sun-drenched sky. But one has only to name him—and that is precisely and solely why I am referring to these folk—in order to appraise Doughty at his right worth. Or glance into another of them: Loti's *Désert*. What of it? A cloying and tinkling performance; as voiceless, almost as voiceless, as a picture on a wall. Where, you ask, where is the shrewd wit, the insight, the humanity of Montaigne? And that other one about Constantinople, or about Morocco: how prettily constructed, how unconvincing! Yet Loti is a writer of renown; there is no gainsaying those exquisite gifts. What militates against his, and his countrymen's, veracity in a personal relation like *Le Désert* is professionalism—and one or two other little things. Lack of humility, for instance; or call it simple imperviousness to foreign languages and ideals. They are curiously incurious, again, as to matters non-human; even the Goncourt's *Journal* is full of queer blunders of observation; they seem to have inherited somewhat from those old Troubadours to whom the human element was everything, and who would now utilise nature as a mere scenic decoration against which to display their emotions, their " sensations d'Orient " or whatever it might be. French schooling, too, does not encourage the seeing eye. Their children are saturated with Racine and other full-mouthed rhetoricians; the

taint clings to them in later years, vitiating their
outlook and making them unduly concerned about
stage-effect—a preoccupation which ruins the
intimate note essential to every good travel-book.

To carry off that intimate note demands
independence; what we call cussedness. Think of
the cussedness of Doughty in doing what he did
among those stark, God-struck zealots; note the
cussedness in every word he writes. Such a man,
strong in reserves, can afford to be veracious, and
himself. His charm resides in sincerity, and you
feel that, however much he gives, he is withholding
still more.[1] Latin authors of the subjective variety
seldom produce that sense of reserve. Their
personalities are less marked, their mutual diver-
gencies fewer, and their reserves, if they have any,
are apt to be blown into stylistic fireworks.

Their personalities are less marked: here lies,
maybe, the core of the matter. The Anglo-Saxon
has a laxer literary discipline, commendable distrust
of authority, a language that lends itself gaily to the
unburdening of extremest individualism; and not
only that. His educational system (despite the
efforts of that old disciplinarian and prayer-monger)

[1] One would like to know, for example, something about the
features of those with whom he came in contact; there are all
too few descriptions of physiognomy in the book. We could
also have been given glimpses into certain secret things, certain
customs of profound significance in Oriental life and of interest
to European students. Doughty, with a kind of maidenly
modesty, barely hints at their existence. Well! A travel-book
is not an encyclopædia.

and the very laws of his country induce him to break
away from the parent-stock. He is centrifugal.
Without abdicating an ounce of self-respect he can
merge himself into anything and assimilate what
you please. He makes a good nomad. His
sympathies with alien races are broad and deep;
there is, at times, something intuitional or prophetic
about them. Could any foreigner have written
Haji Baba? Which of them has looked clean
through the Spaniard like Mr. Havelock Ellis, or
through the Neapolitan as did Charles Grant in his
Stories of the Camorra? And there occurs to me,
at this moment, a volume by Mr. Lowes Dickinson
—I forget its title; quite an unpretentious little
thing; notes, I fancy, from a travelling diary.
Unpretentious, but symptomatic; one questions
whether anybody but an Anglo-Saxon could have
achieved such a point of view. It is to the credit
of our race that, knowing itself to be the Salt of the
Earth, it can yet survey strange people in so benign
and intelligent a fashion. Doughty is another
example of this artlessly sublime detachment.
Will a French Doughty ever appear?

The phenomenon is not inconceivable. Borne
on the wings of opium, or tossed over the sea by
some black fury of despair, a certain one of them
may presently unveil for us the throbbing heart of
the Far East. There, among those steamy forests
and many-hued native folk, he may cut the cable
that binds him to the boulevards; there he may

B

learn to squeeze new and glamorous colour-effects
out of that old mother-tongue, provided—provided
he forgets the solemn Academy everlastingly
engaged upon its blithe topiarian tactics. Must
language, a child of necessity, be clipped and
groomed like a box hedge? Must a living organism
be at the mercy of a pack of dismal gentlemen in
frock coats? Why not let it grow freely under the
sun and stars, to thrive or suffer with the rest of
them, throwing out buds and blossoms, bending to
the winds, and discarding outworn members with
painless ease?

Then appeared the abridged version of *Arabia
Deserta*, of which I promptly bought a copy,
anticipating what actually happened—that another
would soon be called for, and wondering, at the same
time, how many of those to whom this book was a
revelation took the trouble to thank Mr. Edward
Garnett for performing so well his odiously
uncongenial task of dismemberment.

And here is the new full edition.

Moving once more among those sinewy articu-
lations of speech to revisit familiar scenes, I become
aware of a change. Something has happened.
That worldly-calm mood of the 'nineties is fled.
One has travelled in the interval, no doubt, and
suffered, and learnt to see with other eyes. It may
be the inevitable passage of years; that, and our
recent European shattering which affects each of

us in diverse fashion, according to his peculiar mentality.

Whatever the cause, I now go through these pages with a more hearty sympathy for the bedouins —that " merry crew of squalid wretches, iniquitous, fallacious, fanatical "—and a feeling of resentment (others, it appears, are conscious of something similar) against our Occidental institutions; a distrust of those white people who can make such an exhibition of themselves as they have done of late. And now they are multiplying indiscriminately once more, springing out of the earth like the dragon-brood of Cadmus and invading all its fair places, ready to begin again. The world is growing too narrow; congested, and crammed with unpleasantness and deified " masses "; we gasp for fresh air; more deserts, fewer men. For deserts have their uses. Had Arabia been anything but a bleak kind of country, where would our Doughty be? And is he not worth a legion of those others?

From this sense of revolt and dislocation I take refuge in passages like the following:

I had nearly outworn the spite of fortune at Kheybar; and might now spend the sunny hours, without fear, sitting by the spring Ayn-er-Reyih, a pleasant place little without the palms, and where only the eye has any comfort in all the blackness of Kheybar. Oh, what bliss to the thirsty soul is in that sweet light water, welling soft and warm as milk from the rock! And I heard the subtle harmony of Nature, which the profane cannot hear, in that happy stillness and solitude. Small bright dragon-flies, azure, dun and vermilion, sported over the cistern water ruffled by a morning breath from the figgera, and hemmed in the solemn lava rock. The silver fishes glance beneath, and white shells lie at the bottom of this water world. I have watched there the young of the thób shining like scaly glass and speckled: this fairest of saurians lay sunning, at the brink, upon a stone; and oft-times moving upon them and shooting out the tongue he snatched his prey of flies without ever missing.

I re-peruse the opening lines: straightway that exacerbation is stilled.

To hear the " subtle harmony " and respond to the gentle promptings of the *genius loci*, the unseen presence, is what Doughty found to be a talisman. So might others find; but never will, among the unseemly and restless conditions of modern life. Industrialism has been raised to a bad eminence. We do well to take note of certain venerable strains in our being that call for a different environment; our teachers should recognise the inspirational value of self-communion in lonely places. There is in most of us a lyric germ or nucleus which deserves respect; it bids a man ponder, or create; and in this dim corner of himself he can take refuge and find consolations which the society of his fellow-creatures does not provide. The obscure anti-social or disruptive instinct to be alone, which haunts us chiefly in youth, should not be thwarted as it is; for solitude has a refining and tonic influence; there we wrestle with our thoughts and set them in order; there we nurture the imagination and sow the seeds of character. A person who

hears nothing of that " subtle harmony " because his
ears are belaboured day and night by the clash of
other men's voices will never attain to any remarkable depth or insight.   Now those places where the
spirit loves to dwell are made to minister to the
wants of an ever-increasing humanity, the nymphs
are driven from the woodlands, and deserts irrigated,
and everything scientifically explored and exploited.

> There was an awful rainbow once in Heaven—
> We know her woof, her texture; she is given
> In the dull catalogue of common things. . . .

The drying-up of the fountains of mythopoesis,
the elimination of mystery, might well sadden and
sterilise a poetic soul.   And one hears it said at
times that this would be a matter of small moment,
since these inspirers of olden days have degenerated
into a purely ornamental adjunct to life and lost
their authority and significance.   Is there no
prosperity other than material?   It is surely time
to have done with this utilitarian nonsense; to
reverse the proposition and argue, if need be, in
favour of the value of *mere illusions*.   An argument
of sufficient force when one realises, for instance,
that much of what is best in our literary tradition
—that heritage of beauty to which a man will cling
when he has learnt to forsake and deride all his
other natal gods—has its roots in dreams, in nature-
worship, the communion between man and wild
things; and could never have come into being but

for that subtle harmony " which the profane cannot hear." There may well be fewer listeners now than formerly; the din of commercialism is overwhelming; we fail to sense those mild and genial stimulations from otherwhere. Hence our complacency. Hence, too—and this is ominous from another point of view—a considerable shallowness of judgment in practical matters. Thoughts such as these will have occurred to every reader of Doughty. But the subject is not easily exhausted. . . .

I recall my first view of the Chott country, that sterile salt depression in Tunisia, and my feeling of relief at the idea that this little speck of the globe, at least, was irreclaimable for all time; never to be converted into arable land or even pasture; safe from the intrusion of potato-planters or what not: the despair of the politician, the delight of any dreamer who might care to people its melancholy surface with phantoms, mere illusions, of his own. And to-day one reads that an immense tract of South Africa is sinking—yes, sinking into unproductive desert, even as Australia has already sunk. It seems that the rivers out there are not behaving as Providence obviously meant them to behave; they are flowing all askew; in fact, the situation calls for prompt and costly measures if the national exchequer is not to suffer. Long may it sink! May it be utterly unexploitable and uninhabitable to the crack of doom! Then perhaps

Africa will come into her own again, and grow to
be fertile mother of monsters.   *Ex Africa semper
aliquid novi.*   And then will start afresh the now
interrupted reign of those joyous liars who, from
Herodotus onward, have gladdened men's hearts
with their tales.   How many healthy and well-
conducted colonists, think you, could I be bribed
to accept in exchange for a single Sir John
Mandeville?   Good news, too, comes from Arabia.
We learn, not from Doughty but from another
" reliable source," that the so-called *Empty Quarter,*
the Great Red Desert, has not yet been seen by
Western eyes.   Long may it remain invisible, a
solace for future generations!   Deserts have their
uses, and the *Empty Quarter,* let us hope, will
sooner or later demonstrate its *raison d'être* by
stirring that first intrepid beholder, as he gazes
down upon its trackless ocean of billowing dunes,
into some rare utterance—a paragraph or two, a
sonnet, or some poignant little epigram: an epigram
that shall justify the existence of a myriad leagues
of useless sand, and the non-existence of several
myriad useful cultivators.

Let us be thankful, in the meantime, for visions
such as this:

Descending in the steep passage we encountered a
gaunt desert man riding upward on a tall thelûl and lead-
ing a mare: he bore upon his shoulder the wavering
horseman's shelfa.   Maatuk [his companion] shrank
timidly in the saddle; that witch-like armed man was a
startling figure, and might be an Aûfy.   Roughly he

challenged us, and the rocks resounded the magnanimous
utterance of his leathern gullet: he seemed a manly soul
who had fasted out his life in that place of torment which
is the Hejàz between the Harameyn, so that nothing
remained of him but the terrific voice!—wonderfully stern
and beetle-browed was his dark visage. He espied a booty
in my bags; and he beheld a stranger. "Tell me," he
cries, "what men ye be?"—Maatuk made answer meekly,
"Heteymy I, and thou?"—"I Harby, and ugh!" cries
the perilous anatomy, "who he with thee?" "A Shâmy
trading among the Aarab."—"Aye well, and I see him to
be a Shâmy, by the guise of his clothing." He drew his
mare to him, and in that I laid hand to the pistol in my
bosom, lest this Death-on-a-horse should have lifted his
long spear against us. Maatuk reined aside; but the
Harby struck his dromedary and passed forth.

A fearsome apparition; nowise contemptible.
For this desert man cherishes a sense we are in
danger of losing; he feels the need of liberty. See
him riding grimly forth, a law unto himself, while
we sit here in hushed adoration of *orderliness*:
fetich dear to withered, unimaginative folk. Here
we sit, huddled together like cattle in a pen, each
one duly labelled as to his potential worth to the
community, and controlled by a horde of guardians
so increasingly large that the shepherds will
presently outnumber the sheep. Blissful sight!
What is everybody doing? A person who has
tangled himself into so ignoble a knot as to
think our present state of affairs a desirable, or
respectable, or endurable one, who feels thoroughly
at home among the malodorous crowd and bows
the head to all its humiliating extortions and

conventions—what shall be done to such a product of civilisation? Pitch him into the *Empty Quarter!* Deserts have their uses. The desert may yet make a man of him.

Meanwhile I watch with envious eye that Harby, that perilous anatomy, that manly soul and Death-on-a-horse, stalking solitary into the waste, and ask myself whether a few drops of his wild blood transfused into ours might medicine our sickness. Would they heal that valetudinarian itch for being nursed and supervised, and drive out the incubus of duties to be performed towards neighbours undeserving, of sacrifices to be made for causes perverse? Or are we doomed to an imbecile herd-life till the very word " freedom " sound exotic and bedouish to our ears? Britons never shall be slaves. . . . What else are we?

These be the thoughts, somewhat incongruous, engendered by my latest reading of *Arabia Deserta*.

THE CORRECT THING

The Correct Thing

I

NOBODY dreamt that Alberique would ever marry. He was too old, too selfish, too delicate—far too delicate.

Yet now, at the end of two years, his friends were obliged to confess that the union was as much of a success as could have been expected in view of the different ages and characters of the parties concerned. She was almost a child—a child to treasure. For in his selection of a wife he had displayed his usual penetration and knowledge of the fair sex. Silvia, with all those charms to which no one had been more susceptible than her husband, could have done with him whatever she pleased —dissipated his means, turned him to ridicule, converted him into ten times the vicious old devil he already was. She did none of these things: which proved that he had not read amiss the signs of good breeding in her features.

Who was Alberique? Nobody, so far as mere wealth was concerned. Yet not altogether a useless person. While serving under the Colonial Office he distinguished himself by brilliant administrative talents: as Governor of Upper Somnolia, more especially, he had developed a disquieting energy that convulsed the Permanent Staff who still spoke in an awed whisper of that Reign of Terror. All that was long ago! Since his retirement he had devoted himself to certain historical studies, and his writings were appreciated by a select few who could sympathise with his passion for *chroniques scandaleuses* in high places —a passion the origin of which may be traced to a justifiable pride in the many romantic vicissitudes that his own race had undergone. It was one of those families renowned of old for intrigues and escapades and adventures in which, as a rule, the eternal feminine played no inconspicuous part. He ought to have been born in the gallant days of the Restoration. There was nothing in common between himself and the musty ideals of his contemporaries.

For the rest, he had glided through life unobserved by the many. Feebleness of constitution, a hereditary disposition to amorous excesses, were counterbalanced by other qualities envied of most men who can only acquire by patience or bitter experience what he likewise inherited from that long line of ancestors—tact, insight, taste. He was quick to judge of a man's worth as of a woman's beauty. His tact was equal to the most embarrassing situations. Alberique could always be relied upon to do the right thing at the right moment. Self-centred? Doubtless: but courteous at the same time and generous to all mankind, particularly to pretty women. Ill-health unhappily had somewhat soured his temper of late, and drawn more frequent lines about his smooth-shaven, once handsome features. His hair was of the thin texture of one who has lived too well.

They had just returned from a winter in Egypt. The pale, ungenerous rays of an early spring afternoon penetrated through the curtains of their London drawing-room. Silvia, standing at the window, drew them aside to let in more light. She had never found England so gloomy before. She was still dazzled with the remembrance of the glowing sunsets, the desert, the monstrous carvings, and all those other experiences of the last months, for she was none too old to feel wonder, nor too affected to profess indifference. She had been brought up unacquainted with the world, its marvels, its realities. Like some hot-house flower she had hitherto breathed the tepid atmosphere of English society, knowing nothing of the storms of life, nothing of its intenser joys. Impulsive and ambitious by nature, she had early accustomed herself to demure ways.

The recollection of that wonderland of Egypt had aroused new interests in her: vague yearnings, hitherto unfelt, for another existence.

She ventured to open the window, after casting a look to assure herself that Alberique was well protected from the air. Moist warmth poured in, and with it came wafted all the seductive lassitude of spring, the hopes, the fears, the tender longings that penetrate on such days to the soul of man, even through the smoky shell of a great city. A passive life! She had expected more of marriage. She wondered what ailed her. Looking around, she saw contentment everywhere save in her own heart. Outside, the street passengers passed one another briskly before her eyes, each intent upon his own particular duty. The cars, emerging with cheerful din from the bluish haze, splashed through the river of gold at her feet and vanished again like streaks of light. Some children were playing on the glittering wet asphalt. She listened awhile to their merry young laughter, and then closed the window sadly. At such moments Silvia had an intuition of what life might have been. There was a void somewhere, a great void, in her existence. If she were at least allowed to continue her music. . . .

Alberique's voice, frail, high-pitched, but of peculiar charm, broke in upon her meditations.

" You will require cheering up in this melancholy place. You must take to your violin again, Silvia."

" How can I ? " she replied regretfully. " You know the noise—"

" Allow me, dearest, to apologise for my mistake and my unkindness. There is no reason whatever why your pleasure should be thwarted because

I happen to have no sense of music. Sheer
selfishness! But you must bear with me, and
pardon the unamiable caprice of an invalid. You
don't know what it is to be an old wreck like
myself." And he sighed—a very sincere sigh.
" Now take to your violin again, do! I only wish
. . . I wish . . ."

Silvia did not always fathom his wishes. Just
then he may have been wishing for youth, or better
health.

Upon that score Alberique allowed himself to
cherish no illusions. He was approaching the
ninth climacteric beyond which he could hardly
hope to pass. Certain fainting fits had warned him
of serious organic trouble, and the weakness had
become more apparent since his marriage. For
alas, the union, though a happy one, had been in
other respects a grievous miscalculation. Alberique
had drooped and faded away like some tender
flower in that glorious sunshine. He had hoped
to enter upon a second youth, an infusion of new
life. It came contrariwise. He gave all, receiving
nothing in return. The lovely vampire, innocent
of intent, drained away his life. Egypt, he already
felt, had done him no good.

Presently he renewed the subject.

" I suppose, after this long break in your
studies, you will require a teacher again—at least
at first? "

No answer. Silvia was thinking of her former

C

teacher, Lennox, a young Scotsman of more than common talent. Looking back upon the past days of their intercourse, she felt that he had gained more influence over her than she cared to admit.

Indeed the Scotch Paganini, as they called him, exerted a strange power over all who could appraise the high aims of his life. Born of a good family, he had chosen the art of the violin as a profession and pursued his studies stubbornly, with that craving after perfection, that determination to excel, without which genius is an empty name. His infrequent appearances on the concert platform were the signal for unwonted outpourings on the part of the Scottish press. The critics, with patriotic fervour, compared him to some youthful high priest, pale with the scourge of study, about to initiate an unbelieving world into the mysteries of which he was the chosen interpreter. . . . Silvia was wondering what had become of Lennox. No doubt he had already forgotten his former pupil among the interests of an active professional life.

" Why not Lennox? "

She started at the sound of his name. But Alberique was smiling an enigmatical smile. It was really as if he had mentioned Lennox on purpose; as if he had led her thoughts up to this point for some object of his own. What that object might be she could not even guess. She remained silent, but her husband insisted—" What if you wrote to Lennox? "

He was looking at her now in a manner that almost scared her. There was mingled defiance and regret in his eyes. Was it love? Some composite emotion no doubt, that he could not, or would not, formulate.

Why speak of Lennox at all? Why speak of him, the unfolder of her talents, to whom she had looked up with childlike veneration, whose name conjured up the forbidden fairyland of art, whose remembrance she had erased from her young mind not without a sigh? To be permitted to take up music again was almost too good to be true. But why Lennox?

Alberique persisted:

"I have blamed myself all this time for discouraging your love of music. No, don't thank me! I am only doing what I ought to have done ages ago. Forgive me, rather, for having been so miserably selfish. I met him once or twice—Lennox, I mean. Seems a gentleman. You were his favourite pupil, they tell me, and if so, I feel sure you will become his favourite pupil again. You can go on with him, you know, where you left off. He looks as if he could appreciate favourite pupils of your style." Here he laughed, and soon added: "Write to him at once, dear, and make an appointment."

This speech confused her considerably. Alberique had a way of making allusions to her person that were ambiguous, incomprehensible.

She tried to puzzle out his meaning. He seemed to be expecting her to say something.

" Really? " she faltered at last. And then, more resolutely, " Why Lennox? "

" Why not? "

Now Silvia, instead of rejoicing, grew sad. She beheld, advancing towards her, some ill defined phantom that threatened her future peace and happiness.

II

Since her marriage she had never seen the Scotch Paganini. She only knew that at the time of this event he had unaccountably broken off all his English engagements and left London for the Continent in order to perfect his already highly chastened style (so the newspapers announced) under a certain master in the Belgian capital.

This was true enough. There, locked in his room, violin in hand, he wrestled with his old opponent, struggled with the brute material of string and bow; purged away, through sheer physical exhaustion, every other remembrance of life. Here was an adversary worthy of himself, endowed with more than human obstinacy, one who gave no advantages: all the yielding must be on *his* side. . . .

But Silvia did not know—how could she know?—that Lennox now lived like one who, gazing long in the sun, yet sees its spectral image burning wherever his glance may stray; that amid the mazes of Tartini and Saint-Saëns there mingled and floated and glowed persistently, before his mental eye, the picture of her own smile, the golden witchery of her hair.

For his character was primitive as Alberique's was complex. He was one of those men of natural purity who, oppressed with disappointment and temptation, are not led away by the allurements of *Venus vulgivaga*, but cling to their first ideal and exalt it with all the devotion of their simple nature. And in the interval of those two years he had experienced in his own person a singular phenomenon. In proportion as he schooled his judgment and delved deeper into the mysteries of musical art, the image of Silvia likewise became clearer and more lovely. His taste, refined and exclusive, enabled him now to discover charms in her person which had hitherto escaped his appreciation. He could detect no discordant note in that roseate symphony. One might have said that day by day, as the artist grew more discerning, Silvia on her part shook off the attributes of common mortality and resolved herself into the incarnation of all harmony and proportion. From being beautiful, she had become flawless.

And after these visions—the Reality!

Lennox, who used to have faith in his Star and believe in the ultimate adjustment of Fate, was growing sadly despondent. But when, on the eve of his departure for England, he emerged from the long fray emaciated as with monkish self-chastisement, when he had deposited his violin for the last time in its case and asked himself wearily, *what next?*—his eye, roving round the room in a farewell glance, happened to fall upon a letter that lay at his elbow.

It must have arrived that very evening. . . .

If in a moment of self-delusion Lennox imagined that he owed his introduction into Alberique's household to some machinations on the part of Silvia, he was soon undeceived by her demeanour which rebuked such an assumption. To whom, then, was he indebted for the pleasure? He took to observing Alberique closely. But Alberique wore a mask; he had met his advances with dignified ease, and professed to take the greatest pleasure in bringing Silvia and himself together. Was Alberique then, the far-seeing, grown blind? To their duets he often listened with well-simulated interest; at other times he leaned back on a couch, book in hand, and seemed to doze. Perhaps he marched in imagination with the scarred veterans of Pizarro upon some incredible expedition across the Peruvian sierras, or saw himself gliding pliantly, obsequiously, among the gilded pageantry of Versailles. Perhaps—who knows?—he was watching Silvia all the time out of the corner of his eye and extracting a kind of subtle relish from the spectacle of her resistance to his attacks—a malicious amusement, but characteristic of his complex nature. Or was it all generosity on Alberique's part? Generosity to himself? A perverse form of generosity, and a risky one.

But Lennox soon, very soon, desisted from attempting to solve the enigma of Alberique and confined himself to Silvia. He thanked God for this opportunity of seeing her, whoever its immediate author might be, and made the most of it. He was no lover of the sugar-water type. Lennox, the dreamer in Brussels, had changed considerably since his arrival. All the energy stored up during those two years was released at the sight of his ideal. He never attempted to conceal from Silvia the state of his heart; he grew bold, impetuous, reckless.

She was ill at ease. She could not help inwardly blaming her husband for exposing her to this temptation. But whatever her thoughts may have been, her conduct remained irreproachable, although at times she felt her powers of resistance giving way before the passionate desire of the other one. What rendered her defence doubly difficult was his assumption that she had loved him from the first— him, and him only; and that she loved him still. How disprove what she almost confessed to be true? To this embarrassment was added her own susceptibility to an art of which the exponent and personification alike was Lennox, whose genius she revered, whose single-hearted devotion to herself she could not but recognise with respect. Her acute sensibility to music unstrung her reserve and opened vistas to the spiritual eye at which she trembled deliciously. There came upon her, under that spell, visions that she would have bidden linger for ever, visions of a celestial dawn, of the blossoming, as it were, of some proximate, unspeakable bliss.

Looking up in such moments she would find his eyes fixed upon her in a steadfast gaze. He had guessed the truth! And their thoughts thus coinciding, their lips unmoved would say:

" Our joy: our hope—how shall we conceal it from him? "

Conceal it?

Alberique knew everything. He knew of their growing infatuation and its inevitable consequence. But he thought Silvia would keep the Scotsman within bounds so long as he lived, at least; and if they went too far—why, he could easily recall them to their senses with one of his proverbially tactful remarks. Alberique never made a mistake in such matters. He could rely upon himself to do the correct thing under any emergency. Soon enough he would be dead, and then they might do what they liked. Another year or two, and then—the odious change. In the contemplation of that change he recoiled; his worldly yet sensitive mind, that had dwelt long upon the theme of horror, shuddered at the thought of his own body becoming a masterless, meaningless heap: a clod, to be handled irreverently by common persons and thrust at last into a coffin— the end of all things or rather not the end, but only the beginning of a yet more hideous transformation beyond. How inconceivably hateful was the prospect. Alberique was loath to part with life : he had never despised the pleasures of the world; he only deplored his inability, his hopeless inability, to enjoy them as heretofore. Those fainting fits. . . .

To console himself, therefore, he now invented a pastime intelligible only to self-indulgent, hyper-sensuous natures like his own. The temptation had been too strong to resist. The spectacle of those two lovers ready to swoon within one another's arms, a spectacle that would have driven to despera-tion most men in his position, afforded him a voluptuous relish, a new zest in life. He had arranged it specially for himself. Alberique was no spendthrift, no drunkard. At a race-meeting, at Monte Carlo, he could afford to laugh at the weaknesses of his fellow-creatures. Transport him to a desert island, and he would have shared his last crust with some shipwrecked sailor. But to anticipate in the person of Lennox certain joys that he himself could no longer taste; to watch, with vicariously sensual interest, a faltering rehearsal of the drama which would be played immediately after his death—this was an amusement after his own heart.

And he enjoyed the jest prodigiously; its bitter after-taste only served to tickle his appetite. It possessed, besides, the requisite spice of wrongness, of perversity, without which Alberique's pleasures had long ago become insipid. For some time past he had been engaged upon a careful study of their characters. He often looked from one to the other and pictured to himself how they would act—their words, their caresses. Thus, and thus (he would say), thus, and nowise differently. Then he would take note of their present exasperation. It was like perfume to his senses, and almost compensated for his regret at leaving the world.

Yet occasionally he grew tired of his comedy and told himself the truth. He envied their health, their youth. He was afraid of death. And his pleasant little smile would then crystallise into a hard grin of defiance that distorted those still attractive features.

III

It was a remarkably dull tune they were playing. Or rather, no tune at all. Bach, very likely. . . .

Upon an ottoman under a stately drooping palm, his head upon one hand, his feet crossed, he reclined in a calm and languid attitude which had something of the rigid grace of the leaves that shadowed him. Little could be seen of him save the sinuous outlines of his figure.

But he lost nothing of what was going on, and his eyes were fixed upon Silvia when she stood, violin in hand, beside an immense lamp whose rosy shade tinged her white shoulders with a warmer glow. They followed the vigorous motion of her arm glancing in the light, and rested, occasionally, upon her scarlet lips parted in emotion. He surveyed her as a connoisseur might survey some masterpiece of statuary, from her well-poised head refulgent in golden glory down to the dainty feet encased, at that moment, in slippers of a peculiarly appetising description. She was throbbing with young life. The pose, he thought, was absolutely perfect. As for her colouring . . . She had all the loveliness of a Naiad, and nothing of her chill. Oh, yes! There was no denying her beauty, damn it, and if he were only twenty years younger, or even ten. . . . She had actually improved, he thought, since her marriage.

And his glance wandered in the direction of the Scotsman who, under some pretext, had laid aside his instrument and contrived to take up, at the piano, a position convenient for eyeing Silvia. He played a listless accompaniment, accentuating a phrase here and there. Alberique, while admiring the young man's adroitness, began to feel almost sorry for his continued repulses at the hand of

Silvia. In his present cheerless mood he needed some kind of distraction; more movement in the play; a little incident that might have called forth one of his withering observations and allowed him to exult over their subsequent discomfiture. They were such correct lovers. He felt tired, just then, of their correctness.

Lennox, far from being animated, had become grave. He was marvelling at Silvia's music, for she certainly played that evening as she never played before. It was an artistic problem that absorbed him. He had lost sight of the woman and saw only the performer. And as she proceeded, his astonishment at her mastery over the instrument grew apace. He was surprised at her technique and control of expression; amazed at the loftiness of her interpretation. Seldom had he heard Bach unriddled after this fashion. The heated London room, with its atmosphere of weary refinement, was invaded by Silvia's music as with a breath of clean spring air.

Then, gazing into her face, he saw that it was irradiated with joy—transfigured by the magic of love. Her heart came out upon those strains.

The older man had not been slow to detect the alteration in her features and how the dull melody swelled into a pæan of life. His sensitive mind guessed the import of the change. Silvia was breaking down her reserve, casting aside her veil of demureness and assumed indifference, taking the lead and encouraging her lover. Here was a contingency for which he had not provided. How would it end?

He knew her nature too well to think that, once roused, she would rest content with half measures. And what then? As Silvia's husband he had been amused by her secret love for the other; as her master he was irritated by this confession of it. He began to dislike the parade of her beauty; and this parade of her sentiments, under the disguise of music, was yet more obnoxious to him. With a sudden revulsion of feeling he told himself that the joke had gone far enough—too far. He saw his mistake. How amend it? He would gladly have spoken and put an end to the tension. How set about it? Silvia played on, regardless of his menacing look.

And then that thought, upon which he had often dwelt with a kind of insane pleasure, thrust itself upon him in its most offensive aspect.

" I shall be dead soon, dead—the food of worms. Ah, the sinister transformation! And they? Thus and thus. . . . Ah, curse! Curse their folly and my own! "

The blood was leaving his face, upon which a malignant look had settled. His breath came rapidly, and he leaned forwards, grasping in his long fingers a wisp of silken hair. He still endeavoured to control his agitation, knowing its pernicious effect upon his health.

Silvia played on, unaware, in her exaltation, of his existence.

When at last she laid down her instrument, it seemed to Lennox as though a curtain were drawn aside: the artist had melted away from before his eyes and he beheld again the woman whom he loved, radiant and adorable. And he knew the truth. This was her answer to his pleading, an answer altogether plain. Love given and returned: what was lacking? Nothing was lacking save— the occasion. But for the faded, frivolous form crouching yonder. . . .

Meanwhile a profound silence lay upon them all. Neither of the men seemed inclined to speak. Then Lennox remarked:

" A superb rendering."

How hollow the words sounded! How trivial, tactless, almost impertinent—false. False indeed; he should have said *surrendering*. For Silvia knew that she would now yield at the first touch of her lover's hand. Distance of space alone kept her upright. And Lennox was also aware how unworthy his speech had been of the dignity of the moment, but he was determined to break the spell, for in that silence he heard the beating of his heart, and felt himself drawn towards her person by some power stronger than his own will.

Silvia made no answer.

There was another long pause. Alberique said never a word. So far as she could see, he was grinning from ear to ear in a cynical and meaning-less fashion.

The strain became intense, intolerable.

Then she observed with dismay that Lennox was rising to his feet and taking a step in her direction. He came still nearer, trembling with passion. He was now almost at arm's length. Heavens! Had he lost all control over himself?

With a supreme effort she shook off the fascination and remembered Alberique. She quickly faced about and turned to her husband for comfort and support. Gladly enough, in that moment, would she have thrown her arms about Alberique and cried beseechingly in his ear:

"Save me! Take me from him! Save me before it is too late! Once in his arms I am lost to you—lost for evermore. Are you blind? Why sit there and say nothing? Oh, Alberique—one word!"

Surely, she thought, Alberique would redeem the situation. He was notorious for his consum-mate tact. Alberique could always be relied upon to do the right thing at the right moment.

What had he now done?

Alberique had fainted away. . . .

BLIND GUIDES

Blind Guides

BLIND guides are those that cannot see whither they conduct us, those who— perhaps with the best intentions—are apt to lead us astray. And I ask myself whether the youngsters for whom a recently published Life of Nelson seems to be primarily intended are not likely to be misled by a remark concerning our hero to the effect that " during the exercise of his duty as High Commissioner for King Ferdinand he hanged a double-dyed traitorous villain called Caracciolo, and this with a promptitude that Jarvie might have envied."[1] Surely Caracciolo's life and character have been thrashed out by this time! A double-dyed traitorous villain. . . . Are all the investigations of the past hundred years to end in a palpable misstatement of this kind?

It is nonsense, of course; and might have been dismissed as such, had it stood alone. But it does not stand alone; it recurs in one or two other modern biographies of the hero; it is symptomatic nonsense. Symptomatic nonsense is always interesting, even when it only shows, as in this case, how easily

[1] I cannot remember the title of this book or the author's name. It was published in the spring of 1913.

historical writers can allow their judgment to be infected with that gutter-patriotism which ought to be confined to the mob.

If that be not a correct explanation, one would be glad to learn the reason for this modern change of view in regard to the Naples episode. For we all remember the old-fashioned condemnatory judgments of Southey, Palmerston, and their contemporaries; we all know what Foote meant when he wrote : " Be assured, dear sir, that the less is said about Lord Nelson's conduct in the Bay of Naples, the better." Has anything been brought to light in the meantime which might cause us to revise those opinions? On the contrary, minute and painstaking researches by scholars of various nationalities now enable us to approach the subject from fresh sides; and from whatever side we approach it, we are repelled. The local Neapolitan records, as recently disclosed in the writings of Sansone, Spinazzola, Croce, and the rest of them— not forgetting Mr. Badham—read like a nightmare. It was a tyranny, says Lomonaco, " the like of which has not existed within the memory of man."

And this Bourbon tyranny, this unique fabric of vice and incapacity, is what Mr. Gutteridge, another modern encomiast of Nelson, calls " simplicity itself." Mr. Gutteridge has a pretty facetiousness. Briefly stated, the simplicity consisted in this : Thirty thousand citizens, the majority innocent of any criminal *intent*, languished in the prisons of

Naples alone; the executions were so frequent that
the authorities contracted with the hangman for a
monthly salary instead of paying for each execution
separately; without Nelson's active co-operation,
none of these massacres could have taken place.
These are incontrovertible facts. Though some
points still remain to be cleared up—certain documents seem to have been deliberately destroyed or
abstracted—yet the archives are there; they cannot
be distorted; they may be consulted by all who so
desire. We no longer live in an age of oral
tradition.

This is fortunate for those who care to ascertain
data. For oral tradition alone can create demi-
gods—hence their mysterious disappearance in these
latter days of memoirs and newspapers. Were it
otherwise, our British mythopœic faculty might by
this time have elaborated out of Nelson and
Caracciolo a saint and a devil respectively. But
scripta manent. We are moderns. And yet there
is a smack of the dim heroic ages in the labours of
some well-wishers of Nelson, though their efforts are
not directed to such useful ends as those of Hercules
when he whitewashed certain other stables of yore,
nor have they his prospects of success. Why not
take a bolder course and treat Caracciolo as a solar
myth? He was contemporary of Napoleon, and the
thing might be contrived on the lines of Pérès'
"Grand Erratum," that amazing *jeu d'esprit* which
proved the Man of St. Helena never to have existed.

This would simplify matters—in the same fashion, it is true, as the Bourbons simplified the art of government.

Admiral Mahan treats the episode with seriousness, but has managed to involve his hero in a cloud of rhetoric out of which, so far as I can see, two plain statements emerge. Speaking of the execution, he says: " Commander Jeaffreson Miles, of the British Navy, writing in 1843, was one of the first, if not the very first, to clear effectually Nelson's reputation from the stigma of treachery, and of submission to unworthy influences, at this time." And a little later on: " The abrupt execution of Caracciolo was an explosion of fierce animosity long cherished, pardonable perhaps in a Neapolitan royalist; but not in a foreign officer only indirectly interested in the issues at stake. . . ."

Nelson's reputation is cleared; and yet the act is unpardonable.

Cui bono? Who was to profit by the death of Caracciolo? The King and Queen. They hated him. Writes her Majesty: " The only one among the guilty scoundrels whom I do not wish to go to France is the unworthy Caracciolo," etc. And Ferdinand's characteristic echo a day later: " . . . To spare those savage vipers, and especially Caracciolo, who knows every inlet of our coast-line, might inflict the greatest damage on us." But they could not injure him, they could not touch him, without Nelson's help. They got this help, and

Caracciolo was hanged.   A submission to worthy
influences, this?

Mr. Gutteridge, more reckless, speaks of the
" generosity towards his opponents which was one
of Nelson's most conspicuous virtues."   This
language will never do when applied to the
Caracciolo case, which was the murder of an honest
man committed with indecent haste—*a promptitude
that Jarvie might have envied*—and amid other
circumstances of needless ferocity.   To put it at
the mildest, it was an ungenerous and unsportsman-
like proceeding.

The question of Nelson's authority for this
and other arbitrary acts rests upon a quibble
hardly worth discussing.   Though Admiral Mahan
considers the commission under which he acted
" regrettably uncertain," we may all be quite ready
to concede that, from the side of the Bourbons, he
was invested with plenary authority; that with the
fleet to enforce his wishes if required, and their
sentiments so admirably agreeing as to render this
step unnecessary, he received " oral instructions "
from that panic-stricken crew to hang, draw, and
quarter the whole kingdom if he saw fit in the
interests of " law and order."   But we must still
decide whether he was duly commissioned by his
own Government.   In fact, we are confronted by
a variety of questions, such as: Can a British
officer accept similar " instructions " from a foreign
Sovereign?   Or this: Under what conditions, if

any, can the British Government confer authority upon one of its subjects to interfere by force in the internal affairs of a State of peace with itself? Or this: When may an English warship be made the scene of a court-martial upon a foreign officer tried by foreign judges? Also this conundrum, which arises out of Ruffo's simultaneous existence as High Commissioner: Can Ferdinand of Naples, or any other human being, have more than one *alter ego* at the same time? And likewise this one: When is a treaty not a treaty? [1]

These and similar questions will be asked. Meanwhile we may ponder upon this: the blackest of the thousand iniquities of Ferdinand, that of breaking faith with his own people, was committed, and could only have been committed, by the aid of the British fleet. For Nelson was love-blinded from the first moment. On his arrival at Naples, says a contemporary, " the cries of joy were such that one could not refrain from tears, thinking of the

---

[1] The answer is obvious: when it can be broken with impunity. It needs little penetration to see that the words of Ferdinand blaming Ruffo for treating with rebels " contrary to his orders " are an *ex post facto* inspiration of Caroline. Ruffo's position at the time when he concluded the treaty is clearly laid down in the first part of the letter from Acton to Hamilton of June 25th. The displacement of Ruffo by Nelson is due to the fact that the two ladies expected to find the latter less scrupulous in furthering their designs (nor were they disappointed); and in this connection I would echo the surprise of a reviewer (Arch. Stor. Nap. xxix, p. 122) that it should have been reserved for him, the Italian, to discover documents in the British Museum dealing with this case which have escaped the eye of Mr. Gutteridge.

consolation."[1]   But how quickly he undeceived
those oppressed citizens, of whom he naïvely writes
that they welcomed him as " our liberator "!
Micheroux, though he perjured himself for the
worthless Méjean, had at least a certain tolerance;
Ruffo, though he had little tolerance, could at least
respect a treaty; these and other men were bound
to the Bourbon cause by sentiments of loyalty and
the hope of preferment, and yet Nelson the outsider,
who was not paid for his services nor nursed in
traditions of Continental Court-slavery, surpassed
them all in obsequiousness, even to the extent of
becoming chief executioner.   That *Ewig-Weibliche!*
True, he had his material reward, unasked but not
undeserved.

I spoke of Caracciolo as an honest man.   Let us
have no misunderstandings or word-entanglements
on this point.   If honour means anything, then rebels
such as he were honourable men, inasmuch as they
identified themselves with a movement which has
triumphed and gained the approval of posterity.
What are rebels?   They are, says Adam Smith,
" those unlucky persons who, when things have
come to a certain degree of violence, have the
misfortune to be of the weaker party."   It is
therefore odd to think that Caracciolo would never
have been a " rebel " at all but for Nelson's interference in Neapolitan affairs—since the Bourbons
were already muzzled when this saviour of theirs

[1] MS. in San Martino Library, Naples.

appeared on the scene. Or, for the sake of perfect
clearness, I will put it axiomatically: to thwart the
cause of a monster like Ferdinand is the duty of an
honest man. Thus Caracciolo, who deserted what
was wrong to follow what was right (and the rupture
of sundry old associations involved in this step
caused him no small grief of mind), was simply an
honest man.

Nelson reports the execution in a postscript:
casually, as it were. One dislikes this postscript:
It is either disingenuous or illustrative of that
brutality which characterized much of his behaviour
at that time: witness the joke as to *tria juncta in
uno*, or " See that some proper heads are taken off,"
or " Your news of the hanging of the thirteen
Jacobins gave us great pleasure, and the three
priests, I hope, return in the Aurora to dangle on the
tree best adapted to their weight of sins." All this
has a profound significance. The *bête humaine*
emerging under the erotic stimulus of Emma
Hamilton's charms, certain unlovely concomitants
of the older (military) class of virtues make their
appearance, such as the savagery displayed in the
above passages, the ridiculous vanity which at
Naples and Palermo led him to act like some
pampered *prima donna*, and, interpenetrating everything, the flamboyant piety of his sentiments.
In this last respect he resembles many of the
great land and sea pirates who have made
the political map of the world. Impelled by

that blind selective force which makes for efficiency
and of which they are the tangible expression, these
race-instruments are apt to be genuinely convinced
of the Deity's approval of their actions. They do
not hesitate, like ordinary mortals, as to what is best
—they *know;* the " best " is what their instincts
prompt them to do, and it is a quite natural
anthropomorphism that they should identify this
" best " with the wishes of some superior being.
Nevertheless, a few of the mightiest conquerors of
mankind have cherished no illusions on the score
of God Almighty, and it is to be observed that this
kind of phraseology, which sounds well enough in
the mouth of a Mahomet, and was wondrously to
the taste of Nelson, has become rather rare in the
despatches of modern admirals.

" Down, down with the damned Frenchmen " is
perfectly intelligible when one bears in mind that
during those momentous years England lived in a
state of frenzy bordering on insanity. Our agents
in the Mediterranean doubtless failed to realise that,
though we must crush the French, there were nations
to whom French rule was nevertheless beneficial :
nations who, as an Englishman then wrote, would
have welcomed " Satan himself as deliverer " from
Bourbon despotism. Excess of patriotic zeal may
well have led Nelson to execute Caracciolo, or
Sidney Smith to give to the scoundrel chosen by
Caroline for the assassination of King Joseph a
written order enjoining on all British commanders

by land and sea to respect and protect his person.[1] Which only proves that excesses should be avoided.

How far the oppression of Napoleon necessitated the oppression of humane aspirations developing outside the immediate sphere of our warlike activity, might form the subject of erudite disquisitions; certain it is that we have changed our minds since then. Our poets were right and our politicians wrong—as politicians ever will be, when they put back the hands of the clock. We no longer disparage Italians for committing acts upon which we, as Englishmen, have always prided ourselves; we cheerfully admit that in this extinction of national liberalism our Government played the part of the wicked fairy in the tale. It does one good to realise that Nelson was the last, the very last, of his race to be taken in by the Bourbons, and that God Almighty Himself grew to be favourably disposed towards those " rebels " and their perverse strivings. Subsequent events, at least, point to that conclusion.

That being so, why do we seek to round off the anfractuosities of an historical figure like his as if it were designed for some special purpose of fiction? For two reasons, I think. In the first place, we have woven a mystic net of feeling around him and ourselves; he is the symbol of *our* courage, *our* patriotism; and if we hear him accused of anything

[1] See p. 66 of *Le Trame dei Reazionarii*, Naples, 1861.

of which we consider ourselves incapable, such as
the Caraccioli murder, we resent it as an imputation
upon our own characters and exculpate him with all
the shifts and subterfuges which we would employ
in such a case.   And then—his virtues and vices are
those of the old military caste.   The moral delin-
quencies of a great man like Bacon leave us cool,
because he was a thinker whose traits correspond
to a more recent development of our neural
organisation. Bacon was a mere civilian. But
the bellicose disposition of Nelson is a venerable
specific quality, deeply engrained.   Hence the
detachment which is easily accomplished in order
to review the case of a philosopher only succeeds,
in that of a warrior, after something of a struggle.
The roots of feeling, superficial in our sense of civic
honour, lie far down and are hard to disengage
where military honour is concerned.

None the less, were we not so incurably
romantic, we might profitably set up a time-limit for
the deification of heroes.   It may still be odious to
speak the truth concerning the lamented General
Gordon, who brought destruction on himself and
other brave men through disobedience and incapacity; but Trafalgar is a long way off and,
after all, what a relatively small matter it was, this
Naples episode!

It may be said that I am " going for " Nelson
even as Sir H. Johnston lately " went for " Drake.

Nothing of the kind. I care not a fig about Nelson.
I am only entering a humble protest against the
principle of " useful mendacity." My contention
is that as a nation we are quite sentimental enough
and quite sufficiently tainted with Mafeking-
night neurasthenia to enable us to dispense with
such questionable methods of education as are
exemplified in the sentence which was quoted at
the outset. Boys are naturally prone to hero-
worship; the reverence for sheer truth wherever it
may lead is what they ought to learn at college.
Nor am I doubting the writer's good intentions,
which are self-evident; he is making for the best by
the light of inner ratiocination; to instil patriotism
is, *a priori*, a laudable motive. But I question the
utility of falsehood of jesuitical misrepresentation
under any conditions. The end does not justify
the means; and this particular fable about
Caracciolo will be exploded by every lad who
becomes interested in our hero and cares to look up
the subject for himself—with what consequence?
He will learn to distrust and possibly despise an
otherwise excellent teaching system. He will say
what most of us have said: Those masters of ours
—what frauds they were!

Altogether, the time has come when the task of
artificially cleansing the makers of history from
their natural imperfections—the task of dividing
what cannot be divided, an in-dividuality—be it
undertaken in never so charitable a spirit, is one

which no self-respecting man will assume. *De
mortuis nil nisi verum*. We have learnt to
condemn the teaching of many hopeless irration-
alities, and the life of an English admiral is not
to be written after the fashion of the forty—or is
it fifty?—biographies of Saint Patrick. Panegyric
stands on the level of the pious fraud. Shall evil
be done that good may come of it; has anything
ever been gained by denying a well-established
fact? Surely the lesson of all history is that
the propagation of non-truths is unprofitable to
humanity.

That nameless protean evil, which refuses to
see *things as they are*, sometimes takes the shape
of patriotic emotionalism, and then produces an
acute and contagious disorder that can nowise be
tolerated in polite society. It calls for instant
isolation. Fortunately a specific is at hand
nowadays in the shape of that modern spirit
of veracity from which none of us can wholly
withdraw ourselves—no, not even the ambiguous
Mr. Gladstone. So it is worth while comparing
his attitude towards the Bourbons with that of
Nelson. Patriots both, they stand at opposite
poles of thought, and it is quite impossible to
conceive Gladstone writing (another Nelsonian
postscript): " I must beg leave to warn you to be
careful how you mention the characters of such
excellent Sovereigns as the King and Queen of
Naples "; he spoke, if I remember rightly, of the

" negation of God erected into a system." Some
persons, to be sure, are to be considered as
atavisms. Thus, after reading Gladstone's just
and tremendous *j'accuse*, it is well to peruse the
apologists *Gondon et confrères*. No cause so
vile, that some human being will not be found to
defend it.

It has been said that the morality of great men
cannot be judged by ordinary standards. They
create the types; it remains for posterity, that sees
them in their true perspective, to select what is
good, to approve or condemn. I conjecture that
the shade of Nelson is now wandering in meads
of asphodel beyond Lethe, utterly indifferent to
our opinions. I conjecture, moreover, that in
condoning his errors we do not honour him, but
merely dishonour ourselves; that the only thing
which discredits neither party is to seek the truth,
and to speak it, without passion or prejudice. In
so doing, it behoves us to remember that the
Nelson of Aboukir and of Naples is one and the
same person; he cannot be taken to pieces and
separately appraised; he is not a kind of corralline
growth, the minutest portion of which is but a
sample of the whole. The older class of historians
will explain that there are two Nelsons, and
therewith dismiss the subject; as for ourselves,
we grant that he is one and indivisible, but shrug
our shoulders at the hopeless task of reconciling
his actions. In other words, we are like those

mediæval schoolmen who co-ordinated facts instead of subordinating them. When we have ceased to isolate two incidents in a man's life as if there were no organic connection between them—when we can demonstrate Nelson's peculiar mentality to have been such that without Neapolitan abominations Trafalgar could not have been won—then at last history may be entitled to its claim to be called a science.

But our biographers are altogether in an anomalous position. They are better-class ballad-mongers, who sagaciously dispute the fable of Romulus, but have yet to learn that certain new theories of conduct have grown up since they were at school. A few take pleasure in glacial objectivity, in chaste pen-and-ink sketches, and are safe; as for the rest, we read them less for what they write than for what they are. Their moral apparatus—how dim, how far away! If future historians intend to give us canvasses glowing with all the hues of subjective culture and feeling, they should seek out dyes that cannot fade; since that old theocratic system of morality has lost its colour, its many-tinted woof has been bleached into a worthless rag in the dry light of to-day. They must take into their service a new and rational body of ethics; sounder ideas of what is right and wrong, and why it is right and wrong. Unprovided with this, they will remain what they are—anachronisms, museum specimens. They may still

E

succeed in stimulating thought, as does the writer who has led me into this disquisition, but only as warning examples.

This will apply, above all, to the historians of men like Nelson. A large part of the crazy ethics that infect our literature is due to introspection which, instead of purifying, confuses us and produces a hypocritical state of mind that amazes other nations. For it is an open secret that though our English morality, while spontaneous, is of the highest order, it becomes rapidly vitiated by introspection. And thus we get a curious phenomenon, which I should call the lesson of this whole Naples business—to wit, that it is not Nelson or contemporary English politicians who are deserving of blame; they fought for a great cause, and what they did amiss was done in the heat of the fray. Nelson, the unconscious race-instrument, went ahead without much thought and, despite Caracciolo blunders, ultimately made for the best from our English point of view. But these blind guides, his modern panegyrists, in striving to make for the best by the light of conscious ratiocination, make for the worst. He led us to victory; they lead us into the ditch.

For the rest, is it not an astonishing fact that races, in making for this " best," often fall below the standard of the average tradesman? Events long subsequent to 1799 prove that civilised nations are capable of actions towards each other that would be reprobated in a society of Todas. The ethics of modern state-craft: to what hairy anthropoid must we go back in order to find a justification for them? Judged by the outlook of the coster-monger, the violation of contracts, the massacre of the helpless and innocent, are unworthy proceedings. Carried out by brave fleets and with the smiling approval of Almighty God, such deeds are straightway stamped with the hall-mark of national virtue. The fact is, no race has yet been so rich that it could afford to exhibit the ideal of goodness which is frequently observed in the individual. The aggregate community lags far behind its nobler elements.

Yet it moves. New race-qualities arise. We all of us dismiss, as unfit for the job, a nursery-maid who sees ghosts. But not long ago mail-clad warriors and princes of the Church believed in a living devil and other bogies, their minds swaying between insane terror and insaner hopes; existence was little more than a round of litanies and assassinations, its monotony enlivened only by the buffoonery of knight-errantry and occasional visitations of the plague. The mail-shirts doffed, there arose a brood of melodramatic ruffians whose very garments reflect their lack of sobriety; a prey to every impostor, yet hungering, themselves, for every villainy. Let us be done with this nonsense concerning modern effeminacy, with this maudlin cult of mediæval filth and roguery!

Our mental texture, like that of our bodies, is grown both saner and more stable. The callousness of our ancestors is reprehensible in a man of to-day. We find it hard to believe that a few years back our aristocratic ladies were wont to flock in shoals to see criminals executed or to jeer at lunatics in Bedlam—these were the same stout dames who would shriek and swoon away on the appearance of a mouse. Such hysterical brutality may be picturesque, but it is not the stuff to breed from. We demand a nicer sense of measure and decency. And as to the degree of sensitiveness required nowadays, what shall be the test? THIS: A man who can read the details of the Neapolitan massacres of 1799—even in a short *précis* like that of Madame Giglioli—without a feeling of shuddering abhorrence for their authors, shall be considered to lack the nervous organisation requisite for modern needs.

An orgy which, but for Nelson's infatuation for an illiterate harlot, could never have taken place. . . . This is the truth—an ugly truth, and one that will bear repetition, for to be of use it must, in vulgar parlance, be *well rubbed in;* its good effect depends, like that of certain ointments, upon the pertinacity with which the operation of inunction is performed. Or if we prefer to take it in the shape of a pill, why then, in God's name, let us swallow it without further grimaces and endeavour to assimilate it into our system, convinced that it will beneficially counteract the virus of crooked thinking with which some pseudo-historians are trying to inoculate us.

"The list of victims," says Fortunato, writing not in 1800 but in 1900, "is still incomplete—" Enough. We may leave the Market Square with its engine of horror, merely noting, as we pass, that to dub these martyrs " Jacobins," after the playful manner of Mr. Gutteridge, does not alter the fact that no men ever perished in a worthier cause.

What a jovial company they were, meanwhile, at the palace! A little *mixed*, I fear; but what of that, so long as they were happy? Caroline, the Hamiltons, Nelson, Speciale, the adventurer Acton, "my friend and general " Mammone, the drinker of human blood—kings, prostitutes, priests, bric-à-brac dealers, queens, cut-throats, hangmen, heroes—all a jolly family, carousing, hunting, whoring, murdering, lying, praying all day long and half the night: how the immortal gods must have laughed at the fun!

Fun for the gods, no doubt. But, humanly considered, a detestable business from beginning to end. . . .

AT THE FORGE

At the Forge

I

THE sun was rising.

Despite his sixty odd years, old Alf was already afoot; he stood at his doorway, sniffing the air and examining the weather-signs. A cloudless July morning. It had been fine for weeks: it would be fine for ever, apparently. The days were slipping by, one like another, without incident.

"Holding out well," he concluded. There was no fear of a drought in the district, for countless rivulets descended from the woodland heights to refresh the fields and orchards at their foot. One of them ran not far distant through a marshy tract of Alf's ground; a fraction of its waters had been diverted into a pond where ducks were playing about. His eye rested awhile on their movements, and then fell upon a man who was passing along the road.

"Hullo, Henry!" he called out. "What on earth are you doing down here at this hour of the morning?"

"Walking," the other replied, as though that

explained everything.   "Are you coming up to-day?"

"Maybe—maybe; in the afternoon.   Brothers all right?"

Henry was one of three orphan brothers who lived up yonder, on a green, cultivated patch among the beeches, at the Forge.

"Same as usual," he said.   "We'll expect you later on, then.   Nice lot of ducks, old man."   And he slouched away.

What was he up to?

Some mischief, no doubt.   The farmer could not conceive Henry otherwise than up to mischief —he had been the same from boyhood.   But these escapades had grown with his growth, and Henry's name had latterly become a byword among respectable folks.   A great borrower of money, too; probably a thief; but an engaging rascal for all that. Fortunately he was seldom in the country.   He used to arrive like a comet from San Francisco or God knows where and, after recruiting his health at his brothers' expense and getting rid of a "sort of homesick feeling" which, he declared, haunted him even in the gayest capitals, vanish as suddenly as he had come.

Perhaps his elder brother's behaviour had something to do with these departures.   For after the preliminary outbursts of fraternal love had calmed down, they used to quarrel like fiends, and Henry, who prided himself on being a man of the world, was apt to experience some difficulty in restraining his naturally violent temper. Mathew, the senior, had an offensively straightforward fashion of alluding to financial and other delicate matters, especially when he was drunk.

The farmer often found his way up to the Forge, either on foot or on his old grey pony. It was a long walk, and all up hill. He had a sentimental attachment to the place and an interest in the three "boys," as he still called them, since their mother had come from his village and been his playmate in olden days. He never understood why the pretty Joan, who could have had her pick of all the youths of the place, had married that wild man of the Forge, their father. Women do strange things sometimes. Well, they were both dead now, the parents.

Yes, he would walk up that afternoon.

They still called it "the Forge," for such had been its purpose in former times. Now everything was changed. The penurious peasants had at last built a good road that skirted the foot of the hills and defied with stout bridges the floods in springtime, and the old winding path which climbed upwards into the forest between each settlement and then descended again, was now frequented only by summer lovers wandering hand in hand under its tangled network of interlacing boughs, or, in winter, by woodcutters who brought down ponderous beechen logs on their sledges amid the cracking of whips and cheery tinkling of bells. No carts ever passed that way now; it was grown into a narrow green track, invaded by tall weeds, forgotten. And the occupation of the Forge was quite gone—its very name had become unfamiliar to the rising generation.

It was an old-fashioned cottage near one of the many streams that carved themselves a channel down the steep woodlands; a bright garden and a few fields stood around it. And within, everything had remained unchanged for years—its smoky wooden wainscoting and air of mellow prosperity were always the same.

A veritable abode of peace it seemed: so calm and green—so remote from worldly strife. And there was a horseshoe nailed over the porch; Alf noticed it each time he entered the door, and wondered how much longer the fortunes of the house would stand. For they were nearly always on bad terms, the two elder brothers. He was inclined to blame Henry, since the other, whatever his failings, was at least straightforward and honest. Without Mathew's frugal administration, their patrimony would long ago have crumbled to pieces.

Mathew was a close-fisted, bearded fellow of the conscientious-melancholy type, with frequent relapses into boisterous savagery, during which he drank fiercely. He drank not from any love of good comradeship, but from a kind of solitary, ancestral necessity; his father, his grandfather—they had all been drunkards in a respectable, rustic fashion.

Likely enough this primitive trait was what exasperated Henry, who was a convivial and altogether modern creature: frail of body, with burning eyes; easy-going in money matters and temperate in food and drink.

None of the three brothers felt the poetic charm of the Forge like Henry. He could watch for hours the light-effects upon the vast plain below and listen to elfish forest-notes all around. It was a rare change after his feverishly varied experiences of ocean and town-life: he seemed to come back to his mother's arms and to be an impressionable child once more.

For the Forge was wonderful at all hours and at all seasons; wonderful from its sylvan witchery and aerial aloofness from the works of man; never so full of wonder as on those early summer mornings when the hush of dawn, the hush of things to be, still lingered among the dew-drenched beeches, and the plain below, swathed in mists, called up suggestions of a boundless mere surging in amethystine wavelets. Then, from behind the hills, a swift ray of gold would issue, unweaving the mock billows that rolled upwards distractedly, to cling among wet clefts; while all tender things of night trooped away to seek refuge under leaves and stones from the eye, the pitiless eye of flame, that peered down through the green canopy overhead.

This is what Henry would call the "morning mood"; a mood he seldom saw, being a man of fashion and accustomed—save on certain urgent occasions—to rise late.

To Henry the sun was a spectacle—a mere spectacle.

Mathew held it to be a divinely-appointed contrivance for ripening the crops.

And Baby never seemed to see the sun.

Baby was the youngest of the three.

In the exuberance of her joy at the birth of a third infant after so many years, his mother had given him some strange-sounding name, Theodosius or what not, which none of the country-folk could pronounce or remember. So the old one clung to him; and it suited him well enough, with his cherub-face and ever-ready smile.

Their affection for this boy was the only common bond between the two elder brothers.

But, nowadays, the sun never shone for Baby.

Something was wrong with him. The school-master had sent word to say that he was useless at his books. He was changing in appearance, too; his eyebrows waxed thick, and into the blue eyes came a strange light. He still smiled, but it was no longer the smile of lively, ingenuous boyhood; of a doll, rather, or some unfeeling idol. He would have looked well enough no doubt standing bare-armed at the forge, like some young Cyclops, smiting the iron amid a shower of incandescent sparks, for his strength was terrific; but those days were over. The old anvil sat all awry in a jungle of docks and darnels on its mouldy stump, and the few implements that had not been sold were rusting, forgotten, in the shed. Baby meanwhile roamed about aimlessly, and spoke little. And he had developed singular, bloodthirsty tastes which Henry, who had been absent for nearly three years, viewed with considerable disfavour.

"I tell you I don't like it at all," he said to Mathew. "Did you see how he tortured that fowl yesterday? Seemed to enjoy doing it. He's going all wrong, that youngster. I know a thing or two—one doesn't knock about the world for nothing. He's what you call a—"

"We're none of us perfect."

"You're a great man for commonplaces, brother Mathew."

"And you're a damned fool."

It stands to reason that Henry—sailor, mechanic, waiter, school-teacher, and professor of various other polite accomplishments—should know something of the world. But the elder had noticed the change long ago, though he feigned ignorance. He would not allow others to find fault with his charge, regarding Baby's education as his exclusive domain.

Nevertheless, even Alf had observed the same thing. The affectionate child that used to clamber about his knees and fetch him flowers and play merrily among the ducks by the waterside whenever his mother brought him down to the village, had become tainted with a curious dullness. And he used to be so like Joan, formerly, in looks and manner—so pretty, so trim and tidy in his little ways. "He'll keep the house in order," she had once said, "when I'm gone. You should see how neatly he folds up his clothes every night, all by himself. He's my favourite, I can tell you."

No wonder; because Mathew at this time was already grown into a cantankerous youth, dutiful enough and hard-working, but obstinate as a mule, while the other was at sea somewhere—a hopeless vagabond.

It was lucky, Alf thought, that Joan never lived to see this sinister blossoming. Whence had it come?

For there was no doubt about it; the fair boy was growing monstrous; some alien drop had crept into his blood, churning it all contrariwise. Alf was old: he remembered three generations at the Forge, each worse than the last. "Like the rill," he argued, in his peasant-sagacity. "Clear atop—ends in a bog."

And his eye wandered from the contented ducks in their pond to where, all wreathed in the ascending mists of morning, the Forge stood.

Yes; he would certainly walk up that afternoon.

II

"You clear out!" Mathew was saying. "I'll have no dirty thief about here."

Drunk, as usual.

It was his pet theme on such occasions—he always preached, in liquor—and when he attached himself to an idea there was no shaking it out of him. Henry, who was gifted with the rogue's blameless conscience and a goodnatured view of life, was growing tired of this eternal moralising. It got on his nerves. And now, when he felt more than usually cheerful and well-disposed after his midday meal, here was this gloomy grumbler harping on his old string. He tried to turn the conversation.

" I saw Alf this morning. He's coming up later on."

" A fine thing, that brain of yours," the other continued, grimly, " but what's the use of it, if it can't help you to live? Always prowling about after other men's money or their wives. You clear out! And you're spoiling Baby, too. He's all changed, damn you."

" There you're wrong, for once. I like the youngster too well. Who built his forge, I should like to know? You're jealous."

It was quite true. Ever since Henry, in an idle moment, had erected beside the stream a miniature water-wheel that worked in connection with a ceaselessly-palpitating wooden hammer, the boy's awed respect for this vagrant brother had melted into warm love and admiration. Mathew, he felt, could never have built such a wonder.

It was a grand plaything which, for some obscure

F

reason, he called his " Forge." So the name of the
old Forge, that once useful establishment, was still
surviving in ominous degeneration—futile movement, with some little noise.

"Anyhow," Mathew pursued, " you clear out! I
can't stand a dirty thief. Get back to Saint Louis."

"That's no place for an honest man."

Mathew never understood his brother's jokes.

The other, meanwhile, was thinking. There was
some sense in the suggestion—the very same idea
had been in his own mind lately. He was once
more growing tired of the Forge; not tired exactly,
for he loved green trees and fields better than the
smoke of cities, and a life of contemplation had ever
been his ideal; but the place had its drawbacks.
Mathew alone was enough to drive anyone mad
with his moodiness. And he looked round the
room: it was cheerful enough with all its old
ornaments, unchanged for years, shining brightly
and testifying to Baby's conscientious care, and yet
—always the same thing. Henry yearned, in the
intervals between his bucolic moments, for some of
his old pleasures; he was rather too young to bury
himself in this fashion. But, alas! he was a pauper,
and they disliked paupers over there. Here was a
chance.

"Buy me out," he said. "Then I'll go for
good."

The proposal had an unexpected effect upon
Mathew. His glum countenance expanded into a

smile, and presently the man was convulsed with merriment—he laughed long and loud, rocking himself to and fro. It was so heartfelt, so infectious, that Henry caught himself smiling against his will.

"Buy me out," he urged again. "I'm speaking fair."

"Buy you out?" Mathew roared at last. "No! but I'll tell you what I'll do. I'll—I'll—ha! ha! ha!"

He seemed unable to find words. One of his saturnine laughing fits, Henry concluded.

"Well?" he began.

"Buy you out? No. But I'll—I'll kick you out: there!"

"You'll *what?*" Henry had kept his "beastly temper" well under control so far. He knew his beastly temper; it had brought him into trouble more than once. The other, still chuckling hugely, condescended to explain:

"Break your head: see? Can't stand a dirty thief—"

The refrain seemed to please him.

"Dirty thief," the other growled. He was sick of that phrase. "And you? Just a drunken swine."

A hairy arm came at him and smote him a stunning blow on the forehead, between the eyes. That was Mathew's brotherly answer.

Drunker than usual, in truth; for never till now had he raised his hand against Henry. There was a silence, while the younger, dazed with pain and rage, felt a beast within him, struggling to break its fetters. Then Mathew quietly remarked:

" I've had about enough of you "—as if this simple statement were intended to close the incident. He rose unsteadily, and moved towards the door.

The words had roused the other out of a trance: the beast had emerged. Distrustful of his own muscles, he looked around for some means of retaliation. And a shining chisel, hitherto unrevealed, limned itself out before his eyes. It lay upon the table at arm's length, bright and comely; a very handy thing. Henry's fingers closed upon it automatically.

" Not quite enough of me, old man," he replied as, raising himself forwards, he dealt his brother a mad, downward blow that embedded the blade below the skull—there, where head joins neck. Under that impact the firm flesh yielded like water. Mathew collapsed as though his bones had gone from within him; he dropped on his knees, then, slightly swaying, rolled sideways. And there he lay, all huddled up, like the fool he was; with a chisel in his back.

Dead, without a doubt. Dead as a doornail. How easy, how absurdly easy, it had been.

Henry drew nearer and looked at him. There was nothing perturbing in the sight; he had seen dozens of them and they were all alike, more or less, in their stupid way. " You never know what a fool a man can look," a philosophical transatlantic friend had once observed—"never! Not till you see him dead." How true! He remembered the occasion of that remark—the place, the hour; he remembered——

But, by God, this was not your ordinary kind of fool. It was Mathew. The veil was lifting, and Henry's nimble mind began to work under the control of will once more. Those last two minutes were disentangling themselves: out of shapeless sensations they crystallised with scientific precision, like the ice-flowers on a December window-pane, into the hideous fabric of his crime. He had killed his brother. It was a plain affair, though, for aught he could discover as his own responsibility in the transaction, the whole thing might have been an idle dream. How had it come about?

"Get my head clear," he muttered, as he walked to the casement and looked out upon the landscape.

Light: light everywhere—a flood of meridian glory that poured into the world's innermost recesses. Mankind was astir among the fields below, and the chant of ordered life, of things that are, floated upwards from the teeming plain whose variegated crops, sharply defined as the countries on a map, trended away towards a dusky line on the horizon, a belt of forest dimly discernible, where flowed the great river. The land was outspread in a crazy patchwork of green—greens in squares and diamond-patterns—greens lusty and frail; the pride of man, shimmering all velvety under the passionless sun.

The old, old prospect, noonday type of illumination; pleasant enough, but somewhat trite. He had been desiring a change, he recollected—well, he was like to get it now. A fine day, none the less. And a fine day to-morrow. . . .

Suddenly the instinct of self-preservation, heritage of all sane creatures, rushed in upon him, devouring every other feeling.

" I'm the fool, and no mistake! Now for a plan. Think—think! "

He sat down by the table, and thought.

Projects flew through his head, clustering wildly for approval; all the old tricks he had heard or read of; flight, burnings of bodies, buryings, hidings— one more preposterous than another. A complicated business, after all. Baby: that was the trouble. If Baby were to appear at that moment, it would ruin everything; there was no thinking with that boy in the room. And how explain things to him?

He meditated furiously.

A scheme must be elaborated at once and definitely adopted. It was there, the revelation, if he could but seize it; he felt it hovering near at hand, a will-o'-the-wisp, eluding capture. " There's a way out of every mess," another sensible friend of his had once declared, " and a good way, mark you —if they'll give you time to think it out."

Time! there you have it.

And Baby might be standing at the door even now.

" This won't do!" He bored his fists into his temples and his pulses ached with the fiery work of concentration.

Was it gone for ever, that wavering inspiration?

A fine thing, that brain of yours, but if it can't help you to live. . . . Why must the phrase occur to him just then?

And all the while his eyes remained fixed upon the handle of the door, lest it should turn.

What if it turned?

Now he drew a deep breath of contentment, for an immense effort had lured the apparition nearer. It approached shyly, reluctantly—arrayed in all the grace of an angelic vision, herald of salvation. For the merest twinkling it stood erect and eyed him serenely, perfect in loveliness. Yet when he sought to fix the shape upon his mind, those outlines, erewhile convincing, disdained to re-clothe themselves in due habiliments. They were hesitating, elusive.

The main thing, however, was clear.

" Baby," he reflected. " Yes; that's it."

Baby must be implicated; Baby must be transformed into the murderer. That was the glimpse, the celestial revelation.

But how?

Stare as he might, those luminous contours never coalesced again. On the contrary, they were forever melting into new combinations; flowing hither and thither like coloured rills before his eyes, meeting and dispersing in restless bewilderment. He began to feel rather dizzy. Objects flitted aimlessly, reeled and shifted and swam about. Everything moved; there were noises, too. Then the whole room began to sway—it was decidedly sickening.

Faint and gasping, he clutched the edge of the table.

The door-handle was turning, like all the rest.

III

Baby entered, inanely seraphic.

He had been gardening. One arm was laden with freshly-gathered lettuces, while the other wiped the glittering drops of perspiration off his smooth and convex forehead. Perennially moist, this poor tumid brow; summer and winter Baby was too hot, as if, by some flaw in construction, a furnace too ardent had been set within his body. No one guessed what he suffered at night under his blanket. Had he known the bliss of sleeping unclothed on the cool woodland earth like any other wild creature, with the wind playing about his matted curls and chilly dew gathering in the hollow places of his back and shoulders, no power on earth could now have kept him indoors after dark. But his mother had tamed him young; those were joys unknown, undreamed of.

All engrossed with one idea, he made a methodical heap of lettuces on the table. Only then did he turn round and espy his brother near the window and the prostrate form of Mathew lying on the floor. Mathew looked unhappy.

A cloud fell on his face.

" Oh. Hurt himself! " he cried, perceiving the weapon. Baby was acquainted with the chisel's idiosyncrasy; the chisel could cut; the chisel could cut badly.

The other took no heed whatever. He was thinking—thinking. He had regained his composure, and was trying to piece together certain tantalising contours, when Baby's voice briskly broke in upon his meditations:

" Out with it! Here you are. Oh. Blood. . . ."

It was exasperating to be interrupted like this.

There was a pause, and Henry began his labour once more. It was scared, the vision, but the man wooed it fiercely. Now——

" More blood . . . always blood."

Henry pricked up his ears, for the words were followed by low and bestial purring sounds that caused his hair to stand on end. They proceeded from Baby's throat. The sight of that oozing mass had struck a horrid chord in the boy's nature, and all his frame hummed in unison. There was something in the noise that paralysed Henry's initiative: hope sank within him. Turning round, he saw Baby on his knees, bent over the corpse; fascinated, a-tremble.

"Look at him!" he said, addressing some imaginary intellectual sympathiser. "Look at him! How the hell is a man to think seriously with that unholy snarling beast in the room?"

And though Baby's gestures and chatterings, as he continued to gaze upon that scarlet spot, grew more unpropitious every minute, yet Henry failed to read the import of the change; he was merely annoyed at the sight of a human being gloating over a pool of blood. For Henry was temperamentally nice; his sense of propriety was easily outraged, and this behaviour was unquestionably not correct. What was the boy doing?

Baby was staring himself into ghoulish madness. Infernally awkward, anyhow.

Devising plans under such conditions was impossible for a man of Henry's sensitive nerves. The strain became unendurable—would he never stop? It was indecent, this jackal business.

"Get up, you young beast!" he said, giving Baby a vicious kick.

The other rose from the ground. But he was ignited—in man-eating mood, and he took his brother gently by the wrists. Then the snarling began again. At that sound Henry's blood froze in his veins, and all his joints were numbed.

" No, Baby," he muttered, lamely.

The pale terror fled as swiftly as it had come, and he realised the situation. This idiot meant mischief; he must fight for it.

With a wild jerk he freed his right arm, preparatory to dealing a desperate blow. But Baby was left-handed, and that hand, guided by some primordial impulse of destruction, forthwith sped to his brother's throat. It alighted like a caress, in flowery softness; and there grew fast.

The man's blows rained on air; some thirsty vampire, it seemed, was clinging to him and flapping black wings of damnation in his face. Through a confused mist he beheld the lad's smooth features creased into a mask—the very nightmare of a face; all the while, too, there played a joyful melody upon his ears, like the ripple of many waters. Slowly a sombre curtain closed about him. The pæan grew hushed, and he felt himself lifted from earth and borne aloft in the clutches of a fiend.

They had fallen together.

Baby was uppermost, and as he watched how life, the mystery, tripped away under the touch of his fingers, a thrilling sensation, a blissful dream dimly remembered, crept over him. It grew to ecstasy, as though normal passions hitherto sealed up and folded in the wintry texture of his mind were at last, under some exotic stimulus, bursting into flower. All the loves and aspirations denied to his degraded adolescence converged in that awakening, and he would fain have dwelt for ever in its glorious sunshine.

Soon the frenzy melted to a faint languor and dissolved away. Baby's tormented lines relaxed into their wonted bland imbecility; he became himself again and smilingly disposed towards the universe; almost lovable. Still he lingered on the scene.

They were both hurt now; hurt and unhappy looking, and dreadfully untidy. He wondered what it meant. Then, gradually, the sight of those two brothers, who never spoke and never stirred, began to disquiet him. He sprang out of doors, and straightway forgot them. For an irresistible magnet drew him along the garden path where sunflowers beamed benignly; it drew him across a dank meadow, and through the fence to the water side. He sat down on the old, accustomed log.

There it stood, the miracle, the joy.

Shrunk to a summer ribbon of silver, the docile stream was teased through a mazy dance of pipes and passages towards an artificial cataract whereunder, attached to a water-wheel, a hammer was beating a restlessly cheerful measure amid the splashing of angry little waves. That hammer! There was nothing like it on earth. Other delights swarmed about the building; other wheels, and a palisade by the shore, and pointed stakes to impale storm-tossed leaves and grasses, and a microscopic window through which you could look down upon the deluded current gliding to its fall—but this was the chiefest of them. It was a never-ending marvel: the beating heart of the Forge. Ceaselessly, night and day, that pleasurable din resounded; come when he might, at sunrise, noon or evening, the wheel never tired of its playful somersaults, nor the sprightly water of licking those smooth round sides.

Of the original structure hardly a trace was now visible; the boy's successive embellishments had transformed it into a symbol of his own mind—an agglomeration of scraps of wood and iron, encrusted with nails, and submerged under a wilderness of wheels that fulfilled the inscrutable purposes of his architectural phantasy. There were ornaments everywhere but never, never enough. The problem where to affix them was one on which his brothers were always consulted, and nothing pleased him better than when Mathew sagaciously shook his head and bent down to correct some error, while Henry approved in lazy and jocular fashion; or when Alf would slap his back and say:

"That's right, boy! Now for another wheel."

For Alf was his friend from earliest childhood, and took a keen interest in the masterpiece; he noted everything.

Baby looked up and there, sure enough, was the kindly, grizzled face of the old farmer peering upon him over the palings.

" Hallo, Baby! " he said. " Let's have a look at the machine."

He entered and examined the works critically.

" Who moved that post? " he inquired, pointing to some innovation.

" Mathew," said Baby.

" Where's Mathew? "

" Inside. Hurt himself."

" Hurt himself? What d'you mean, boy? "

That was the extent of Baby's information.

Alarmed by these words, the farmer walked to the house-door and entered. The level beams of the sun poured into the chamber and fell upon certain glistening patches on the floor. And he saw the tragedy. The two brothers lay side by side; so Baby had willed, like a tidy boy. Things lying about should always be tidied. But their eyes were staring and their mouths agape, for a contingency so remote had not been anticipated in his mother's scheme of education.

Alf stood aghast. Then, by an effort of will, he broke the spell of horror and, tottering from that tainted room, sat down on the bench beside the porch. The sight of that transfiguration had made him sick at stomach.

A long while passed, and still he could not collect his thoughts. Despite the fearful picture engraved upon his vision, he failed to acquiesce in the full truth. " Hurt himself. . . ." A lie, of course. There was a practical side to the matter, then. It dawned upon him in furious intensity. He must act without delay.

Baby was watching from afar. Then he approached and again halted, for he could read trouble and displeasure in his friend's face. He came a few steps nearer, like some diffident animal, and waited once more. The farmer looked into his eyes.

He remembered Joan, and olden days.

" Oh, Baby! " he said. " They'll hang you for this."

After these words he was stricken dumb. Another wave of feeling was passing over him, a wave of shuddering hatred, the loathing of the pure for what is impure. All the traditions of his race, all the uprightness of ages of decent law-abiding culture, surged up within him against this pestilence, this savage, this ravisher of a fair human life. He would tell the news in the village; men must bring down the bodies and arrest the brute. He rose from his seat and strode down the path.

The other could not believe his eyes. He stood leaning against the sunny paling, one hand outstretched to bid farewell, petrified with amazement. The farmer walked away without so much as looking round. Never before had his friend behaved after this manner. Something was wrong, very wrong, with the world. And now he was gone, actually gone. . . .

The old man had not proceeded far under the

trees before other counsels prevailed. His simple heart, all puzzled and distraught, yet found the right formula. "After all," he thought, "he's only a half-witted child. They'll never hang him. And he'll follow me like a dog."

He returned anon and said authoritatively:

"You come back with me. Now."

Baby seemed to ponder the meaning of these words. Then his glance strayed in the direction of the stream and rested on a well-known spot.

He shook his head. How could he leave the Forge?

Alf divined his thoughts. He entered the shed, and presently came forth again, bearing a large sack.

"Look here," he said. "We'll pack your machine into this, every bit of it, and you shall carry it down and set it up in my water. . . ."

The other listened and understood. His Forge was to be taken away—a world of unhappiness! Cowed by the man's firm demeanour, he said nothing, but his eyes glittered dangerously and he refused to stir from his place.

"Where the ducks are, you know."

Even that did not move him. Sullen and defiant, he looked on as the wheels and ever-industrious hammer, the pipes and boards, all of them, one by one, were torn down from their old places and stowed away, in darkness and confusion, within the sack. All too soon nothing remained to

show where the miracle had stood; nothing save
four mighty piles, firm-planted by the shore, among
the stones.

The little brook, leaping to its forgotten channel
in a passionate eddy of joy, bore off the muddy
stains of human interference and sped away
gleaming.

"Come along, Baby; and carry the sack. It's
getting late."

And they turned their backs upon the old Forge
and crossed the familiar bridge, the first of many
on that winding woodland path. Neither spoke a
word.

The hush of evening, of things that have been,
was already nestling among those dreamy upland
beeches. But through the gaps of their far-
spreading foliage they beheld, down below, another
and almost fabulous world, a world of liquid gold,
that still throbbed with life. For the sun was
sinking in a radiance that drowned the colour-
mosaics of noonday, and at their feet the plain,
interwoven like some praying-carpet with arabesque
delineations of roads and hedges and waterways,
lay weltering in hazy leagues of orange-tawny
splendour. Then a calm fell from on high, an
apostolic peace; it streamed earthwards in showers
of dewy benignance, and now nothing told of
mortal man save where some window, smitten by a
lingering beam, flashed into the twilight its fugitive,
crimson conflagration.

G

The evening phase. . . .

And still neither spoke. The farmer trudged along, weighed down by a load of perplexities to which his long life's experience could suggest no solution. Since that morning, when he had stood at his doorstep and glanced up at the Forge all veiled in ascending mists—what an eternity had passed! And the days, of late, had been slipping by; one like another, without incident.

He thought of Mathew, whose moral worth had always appealed to him; a drunkard but a right-minded fellow; that was past gainsaying. As for the other—the use and beauty of Henry's perverse intellectual gifts had ever been a puzzle to the old man who viewed human affairs from a fixed point, as he viewed the stars; an enigma, a blot in the world's contriving. Yet in the recollection of those poor distorted remains he grew more charitable; the ways of God are dark indeed, and—who knows? —without men of Henry's stamp there would perhaps be no honest folk. And then the third, with his attractive face. . . . Baby, a murderer! The evil mood returned.

His companion, bent under a heavy material burden, was stepping blithely forward. Maybe he had visions of a consoling kind—visions of another Forge-installation, of a sandy beach where amiable fowls disported themselves on quaintly-fashioned feet or paddled sententiously about the water. It never struck him that his miracle would be mute and motionless in that stagnation: its foolish little heart at rest. And still they marched in silence. Once or twice the old man stopped short as though to say something, but he evidently thought better of it.

Darkness meanwhile came on apace. The blue woodflowers waned to pallid spectres under its touch; chill breaths of wind were creeping down the gullies. Their path grew ever narrower in branch-charmed mystery, and when at last they emerged under the purple dome of Heaven, the lights of the village had begun to twinkle.

EDGAR ALLAN POE

Edgar Allan Poe

MUCH has been written of late concerning Poe, but his personality splits up so much more easily than that of other authors into separable fractions, that it is still difficult to estimate him as a harmonious whole, an individual. There is the Poe of French writers, the Poe of Griswold, the Poe sane or insane (to adopt the classification of Mr. Willis), Poe the critic, the husband, the drunkard, the martyr and so forth. Professor Woodberry has disentangled and rearranged certain of these aspects with patient but chill discrimination. To present them in such a manner that their coherence is seen to be inevitable is the task of a literary biographer; but before the fabric can be erected, each part must be considered and appraised in its relation to the whole. Poe's views, for example, upon domestic architecture and furniture are pronounced; they form a minute but integral portion of himself. Until they have been judged in their relation to the other portions, and traced to their sources in his reading, his age and his heredity, how shall the picture be complete?

Nor can his literary personality be regarded

otherwise—at this time of the day—than as an expression of bodily organisation. Enough and to spare has been written upon certain aspects of his moral life. We all know that he drank. But not all critics are yet equipped with a knowledge of the pathology of mind sufficient to enable them to pass judgment upon the sombre, lovable and mysterious being, as he is depicted by those who sympathised with him in the closing years when he was tossed on an ocean of vain hopes and vain regrets. Who is not moved by Mrs. Weiss's account of that visit to the Hermitage? Some of Poe's epistolary effusions, on the other hand, leave a bad taste in the mouth. His last years both as a man and a writer are full of jarring notes, of conflicting elements which must be separately analysed before they can be welded into a homogeneous whole. Not every critic possesses the requisite sensitiveness, veracity and sheer learning for this work of reconstruction.

The " good woman," unfortunately, has a knack of coming too late upon the scene, and when at last she does appear, she is apt to eke out lack of sense with superfluity of feeling. Such was not invariably the case with the tender ladies whose names are associated with Poe's later life, yet they certainly failed to understand the case of Edgar Poe as a whole: how else shall we explain the posthumous publication of his miserable outpourings to them? Such an act savours little of wisdom or womanly modesty. To brandish aloft the scalp of a conquered

enemy may suit the humour of a redskin, but not of
a civilised lady who has been honoured with the
confidences of a distraught and dying genius.

There is Poe the American, whose patriotic
labours have perhaps not been sufficiently appreciated
by his countrymen. It is not easy, nowadays, to
realise the low position which American letters then
occupied in the world's opinion, and the slavish
adulation with which every product from the European literary market was greeted in the United
States; not easy, therefore, to estimate the extent
of Poe's labours—how he encouraged American
writers of every stamp, coaxed them, drove them,
pushed them the way they should go. Some talk of
his "regrettable scarification" of the New York
literati. They must have been a thin-skinned
generation, these *literati!*

"Is there no honour—no chivalry left in the
land? Are our most deserving writers to be forever
sneered down, or hooted down, or damned down
with faint praise?"

That does not sound like scarification. Taking
his criticisms one by one, it will be found that the
proportion of favourable, indifferent and unfavourable is, approximately, as 3 : 2 : 1—showing that
for each unfavourable review there were five not
unfavourable. Surely this is a high allowance,
considering the quality of the material before him.
An equal number of similarly incapable British
scribblers would not have been let off so easily.

One author is surprised that none of his critiques is "unreservedly laudatory." This simply means that they are conscientiously written.

Essentially, however, Poe was both non-American and non-English. The promptings of his blood were Celtic and Latin. He had a classic sense of analysis, form and measure. For this *justesse* he has been held in high repute by French writers and it is certainly not without a feeling of propriety that he has given French names and extractions to the heroes of his tales of ratiocination (Dupin, Le Grand). Truth *versus* Goodness is the keynote of his intellectual strivings. He had a bald love of truth which puzzled and pained many good folk. Lowell observed that he " seemed wanting in the faculty of perceiving the profounder ethics of art "—in other words, that scientific criticism, as Poe conceived it, is in a manner un-moral. Lowell, to be sure, wrote in 1845. But Mr. Stoddard has also remarked of some of Poe's tales that " the power of such writing is certain: its good, its sanity, are not so certain."

Are we never to grow out of this doctrine? A healthy person, who refuses to be hampered with preconceived notions of wrongness or ugliness, will find that Poe's ghoulish tales, like many "unhealthy" writings, deal with interesting subjects in an interesting manner. What more shall be expected of an author? Doctors tell us that hyper-sensitiveness in the matter of what is morbid or

immoral is far from being always a good sign. And
it has ever been the misfortune of writers possessing
mathematical consciousness of purpose that they are
exposed to the criticism of others who, in their
anxiety to save their souls from hell-fire, have not
acquired the mental outfit necessary for grasping
their initial proposition.

A consideration of Poe's tales would be a good
occasion for discussing the question of local colour
in fiction. Where precision in data is required, no
one is more precise than Poe. But it seems to me
indisputable that, for the subjects generally chosen
by him, his own indefinite atmosphere is the most
suitable. To-day this is a matter of sentiment, but
the reader of the future, approaching these questions
with increasingly scientific canons of taste, will be
enabled to draw increasingly truthful conclusions
from them.

There is a more general agreement that Poe was
right as regards the length of his tales. The
English public alone continues to think somewhat
strangely upon this subject, for a generation fed upon
the gross fare of the Victorian epoch has naturally
acquired a palate too vitiated to savour the delicacy
of simple tales. To them such *entremets*, which
none save a real chef can prepare, are things of air—
things French, dilettantish. And yet, as if to
convince them of their error, the English language
boasts of some of the finest specimens of that ideal

microcosm, the short story. Its proper length is suggested by the organic laws of our own body—one hour's continuous careful reading. The author must be allowed time to engross, by means of his intellect, that of the reader; for a short story is a self-consistent entity, with head, body and tail all complete, and not a mere " taste of your quality "; yet if it be too long, the reader's attentive faculty is strained beyond the capacity of æsthetic appreciation. In this form of composition, the author will exercise a judicial sense of measure; in the more personal prose poem, which conveys rather certain fleeting dispositions or emotions, he may allow free rein to his fancy, his humour, his erudition, his spleen—so long as he attains his end: the awakening, in the reader, of a particular mental mood. If these rules are correct, it will be seen with what unerring instinct Poe conformed to them in both these classes of composition.

His women have been described as imponderable. Yet they are not, like many women in fiction, evanescent. Ligeia is a phantom, but a phantom that has come to stay. I confess that it needs a robust imagination to conceive Berenice smoking cigarettes and eating strawberries at a picnic. Morella was not much of a flirt. They are hopelessly unfit for the ordinary routine of life, for charity bazaars and the bringing-up of children; they have nothing of that air of probability which distinguishes our flesh-and-blood acquaintances. Perhaps for that reason they have ceased to be nonentities. A few more such shadows might profitably be acquired in exchange for a herd of our amazingly *lifelike* heroines of fiction.

It is not to be supposed that Poe ever came in touch with the East, but his artistic feeling suggested to him both its uses and its limitations as a subsidiary ornament. He lacked the broad human sympathy requisite for writing Oriental tales; he never attempts to smother us in harems and such-like paraphernalia. Like the flakes of gold in the chinks of some faded masterpiece, the Orientalism of Poe is so sparingly dispersed—an almost imperceptible touch, here and there—that none save a connoisseur is able to feel what the loss would have been, if that touch had not been given. Note, likewise, his parsimonious but judicious use of the Gothic: " Some large, old, decaying city near the Rhine "; or " The pomps and pageantries of a stately Court, and the mad clangor of arms . . . oh, bright was the seraph Ermengarde! " What an instantaneous disposition of mind is awakened by this artifice! Yet it is a singular fact that Poe was deficient in all sense of the peculiar lustre of Gothic and Saxon words; his prose is redundant in Latinisms which weaken its effect incalculably, though the formal solemnity of some of his compositions is thereby enhanced. Strange to think that, in a matter of this kind, Herbert Spencer (" The Philosophy of Style ") should have a truer insight than Poe the artist.

Monsieur Hennequin has insisted upon the originality of Poe. He *is* original—he is always Poe, although some of his tales, like " Hop-frog," " William Wilson " and possibly " The Landscape Garden,"[1] can be traced to earlier sources. From the first to the last of his writings is revealed little change in the texture of his mind. " Eureka " is embedded in " El Araaf," " Eleonora " in " Tamerlane." In " Landor's Cottage," one of the last of his studies, will be found reminiscences of at least six previous tales. Poe was prodigious in intellectual versatility—in variety of material, singularly poor. But this organic poverty must not be confounded with artificial simplicity, with the deliberate repetition of set words and images whereby the haunting charm of his verse and tales is often contrived. Perhaps, under the influence of stimulants, there arises a tendency to reproduce identical modes of thought; even as a dream, interrupted, may be resumed when the conditions which gave it birth are repeated. It is probable that some of his best writings are the direct result of alcohol.

The " Assignation " (" The Visionary "), an

---

[1] A. J. Downing. A Treatise on the Theory and Practice of Landscape Gardening, Adapted to North America, with a View to the Improvement of Country Residences. 8vo, 1841. I have not seen this work, but I understand it has little in common with Poe's story. Yet the title may have given him the idea. Pückler-Muskau, Lenne and others had made the subject popular.

early and relatively poor performance, is in this respect perhaps the most characteristic of his tales. It reeks of alcohol; it displays alike the power and the weakness of the delirious imagination which flows from the bottle. The reader is oppressed with I know not what sense of distortion and dislocation. There is a restless flicker of fantastic metaphors and inconsequential interjections. Sometimes the imagery glows in steadier blazes, as in the fine passage beginning " The eye wandered from object to object, and rested upon none," which is further interesting as exemplifying Poe's dearth of material —the *carvings of Egypt* recurring in " Ligeia," *convolute censers* and *trembling draperies* likewise; *crimson-tinted glass* in " The House of Usher " and in the " Philosophy of Furniture," *carpets of gold* in the last-named and in " Ligeia "—and so forth. An unusually good " alcoholism " occurs in " Monos and Una ": " Issuing from the flame of each lamp (for there were many) there flowed unbrokenly into my ears a strain of melodious monotone." Future physiologists may investigate what condition of the cerebral structure is requisite to produce an image of this kind.

What is Poe's life-work? His influence upon literature as a civilising and purifying agency. Poe is a great anti-vulgarian. As such, he has discarded the ethical moment, and in doing so, he has followed the footsteps of the masters of all

ages.   Why is it that didacticism in poetry was
so offensive to him?   Because it constitutes an
intrusion of ethics into art, an intrusion which
arouses, even in ordinary minds, a sense of
incongruity and impropriety.

This whole question of morality in art is
neither too difficult nor too delicate to be probed
to the bottom.   Philosophers may grow grey in
theorising upon the growth, the laws and limitations,
of the moral sense of mankind; but there is, and
there can be, nothing new about morality in the
ordinary acceptation of that term: the whole body
of it is reducible to a single word—charity—and
that word is plain to an infant's understanding.   To
burden dainty verses with a load of maxims
regarding the inadvisability of coveting one's
neighbour's wife and other matters that we babbled
on our nurses' knees is as incongruous as serving
tripe and sausages (healthy fare, no doubt) upon a
platter of Benvenuto Cellini.   There is no *poiesis*
in a didactic work of art, and whoever eliminates
the moral moment will discover often that he is
eliminating, simultaneously, the vulgar moment.
For morality is the property of the crowd; it bears
an inscription that damns it for all purposes of art:
connu! The minutest hint of a moral lesson is
a generalisation: generalisations cannot awaken
emotions like single images, and therefore morality
should not intrude where the awakening of emotion
is the primary object.

Without professing to any special knowledge I should say that Poe's influence upon the development of American letters is somewhat underestimated, not as a direct model for prose or poetry, but in a general way for the principles of truth and honesty laid down by him that are naturally difficult to trace to their source, seeing that they have become so thoroughly assimilated by the national literary mind that it forgets whence it drew them. They have indeed become part of the mental atmosphere necessary to every decent writer.

But he has had a number of direct imitators. " Hans Pfaal " has inspired Jules Verne, and the Sherlock Holmes series could not have arisen but for Poe. The author of that series has thought so highly of him that he has embodied the spirit, or spiritualised the body, of another of Poe's tales (" The Cask of Amontillado ") under the title of " The New Catacomb," in the collection known as *The Green Flag.*

Some authors, Mr. Andrew Lang among them, have suggested the question whether Poe was not born at an inopportune moment; meaning, presumably, that under other circumstances of time and place he would have met with a more sympathetic reception. Likely enough. He exemplified, in more ways than one, the irruption of an older type into an immature stock, and suffered accordingly. For at that period of national growth there was little tolerance of

H

anti-social habits in the cultured society
of the States; the phenomenon known as the
New England Conscience seems to have been,
geographically speaking, less localised than at
present. But this ill-treatment of Poe by his
contemporaries has been absurdly exaggerated.
It would be nearer the truth to say that he was
surrounded by firm friends of both sexes who helped
him whenever they could, and who defended his
memory with quixotic ardour after death, though his
peculiarities while living must often have repelled
and exasperated them. It is frequently said that
the time is not ripe for this or that man of genius.
If one cares to pursue this line of argument at all,
it may pertinently be asked, where is the time or
country that needed Poe as badly as the America
of 1830?

Mr. Briggs once made a remark which seems to
express a still current opinion, to the effect that
Poe had " an inconceivably extravagant idea of his
capacities as a humorist." I cannot but think that
this whole aspect of Poe's literary career has been
wrongly interpreted. Poe, to whom pecuniary
assistance in moments of direst distress was galling,
probably simulated this opinion of himself in order
to hide the true state of affairs, even as he is known
to have assumed relative affluence to dissimulate
his poverty. It is hardly conceivable that he
should have been mistaken in his self-analysis—
he knew better than most authors his own strength

and weaknesses. And among his deficiencies is certainly to be reckoned a total lack of humour.

Like many individuals of flawed brain-structure, he took himself *au grand sérieux*, and could not unbend to laughter. He never passed out of the " misunderstood " stage :

> From childhood's hour I have not been
> As others were—I have not seen
> As others saw—I could not bring
> My passions from a common spring.

Thus sang the boy, and felt the man. But it is unlikely, I think, that a writer of his exquisite sensibility could have written these " humorous " sketches with any other feeling than repugnance ; he must have writhed while prostituting his pen for this drivel. Yet it was paid for, as we know, at the same rate as his best work; and starvation was the alternative. The sad multiplicity of these tales of humour would proclaim his frequent and extreme destitution, did we not know it from other sources. "We have now got four dollars and a half left. To-morrow I am going to try and borrow three dollars, so that I may have a fortnight to go upon."

Though the world, alas! has seen other cases of a strain of humour appearing under a strain of hunger, it is not easy to discover more piteous documents than these particular tales of Edgar Poe. Baudelaire, who was joined to him by elective affinity, or, as Poe himself would have expressed it, by " sympathies of a scarcely intelligible nature," has hit upon a happy phrase for this unhappy state —*les stérilités des écrivains nerveux.* And how aptly De Quincey, himself of this class, has described that agony of paralysis, that anguished suspension of all the powers of thought:

Suppose the case of a man who has helpless dependents of this class upon himself, summoned to face some sudden failure of his resources: how shattering to the power of exertion, and, above all, of exertion by an organ so delicate as the creative intellect, dealing with subjects so coy as those of imaginative sensibility, to know that instant ruin attends his failure.

Might he not have had Poe in his mind's eye during one of those moments when the poet stood, helpless and distracted, beside his wife, who lay dying upon a straw mattress with not even a blanket to protect her from the wintry frost? Under such conditions, that lasted for months, let any man of feeling endeavour to write the " Rationale of Verse."

In judging of Poe's sufferings, his own nature, that intensified them a thousandfold, must not be left out of account. The stupendous Beethoven is the most awful example of such a fate—awful from the contrast between the sublimity of his mind and the meanness of his daily cares. But Beethoven had lighted his torch at no earthly altar; he was no mortal, but a Titan, smiling with

BELLADONNA

Belladonna

Miss Dorothy Melville to her Mother

MY dearest Mother,—I am quite well and
I hope you are the same. When are
you coming back? Please come as
soon as you can because you have already stayed
away so long. It has been raining hard for the
last two days and I am nearly always indoors.

Aunt has just been here and has read this letter
I am writing. And she says she would gladly take
me to you if you would allow her. But she also
said that I am no trouble to her and that she will
keep me here as long as you like and that she will
write to you in a day or two. But I do so want to
be with you.

And she also says I am to write and tell you
exactly about the two Fortescue children, although
it will take me an awfully long time to do so and I
think I shall never do it. But she says that you
will wish to hear all about it as you know their
mother well who has always been so unkind to them,
and Aunt says I ought indeed to be thankful to have
a mother who is not like theirs. So I met Bertie

Fortescue on Friday morning. And you know he is only a little younger than I am and ever so nice and I have been playing with him and his sister Daisy almost every day since you left. But I never liked Daisy so much as him because she often spoke so naughtily although she is only five. And then Bertie told me " Let's go for a run to Oakley Woods " because you know he and Daisy are nearly always alone and their mother does not mind a bit what they do or where they go to and their nurse has her holiday. So I said yes and we went, but when Daisy saw us go she shouted so much that we had to take her too. And when we got there Daisy found a beautiful little cherry-tree with black cherries growing all over it which I never saw before, and she said they were wood-cherries and that because she had found them she was going to eat them all by herself. But I told her she was greedy, which indeed she always was. And then Bertie said : " I say. I know. Let's have them for tea all three of us this afternoon and let's invite mother as well, and let's pretend and send her a real invitation as if it were a real party." And so Daisy thought a bit and said:

" All right. Let's pretend."

And she got all the cherries, lots of them, and filled them into Bertie's sailor hat and got her hands ever so messy with them. And we carried them home to their room and never let her eat a single one of them, and hid them in their old doll's house.

And then they asked me to write a real invitation, because I was the eldest, for them to leave on their mother's dressing-table. So I wrote it out just like this:

" Mr. and Miss Fortescue desire the presence of Mrs. Fortescue at tea this day in the old Nursery. There will be cherries."

Then Daisy went and pinned it on to her mother's dressing-table where she knew she would find it soonest when she came home. I could have written it much better for them, but I had no time as I had to run back to Aunt for luncheon. But at luncheon Aunt told me that I could not go to tea with them because she had promised to take me to see old Mrs. Helyar that very afternoon. So I ran and told them about it.

And then they told me their mother had also said she would be away the whole afternoon and could not come to their party and that they were to mind and be good children and that her maid would take them for a short walk at half-past two and that afterwards they could have their tea alone and do what they liked. But Daisy said she thought it nasty of her mother always to leave them alone or to send them out walking with her nasty maid. So Bertie got quite angry with her and said " What will Dorothy think if you go on talking like that, you know you mustn't, Daisy." But I believe he thought so too.

At last they said they would arrange the party

just as if I and their mother were coming all the same and pretend we were there all the time.

And when Aunt and I drove home from Mrs. Helyar's it was nearly seven. But Aunt allowed me to stop a moment at the Fortescues' house, because I had told Bertie I would try to come and see them when they were alone again after their party. So I ran along the drive and up the steps and into the house, but did not see either Mrs. Fortescue or anyone else in the house, although I heard the servants below. And then I went up to the old nursery and saw that they had eaten all the cherries from an empty plate on the table. But Daisy was lying on the floor with her hair all over her face and never spoke a word to me. And Bertie sat still in a corner of the room. Then I thought they were only playing some game and pretending, you know. So I went up close to him, but he looked quite white and his face was so unhappy that I got afraid and ran downstairs to Aunt. Then she went up to the nursery and came down again and sent some of the servants for Mrs. Fortescue and drove herself and fetched Doctor Symonds in our carriage and sent me away home alone on foot. So I wondered what was the matter. And when Aunt came home she told me that the Fortescue children were both quite dead and that I must never see either of them again. And Doctor Symonds came later in the evening and asked me a lot about those cherries. He says they were not at all real cherries, but he thinks they must have been planted by the wind from the seed of some plant which Major Arbuthnot brought from abroad long ago into his garden. You know he is the man who looks so like poor father.

And Aunt says it is funny that a man who looks so like poor father should so nearly have been the cause of my death, as if father already wished me to live in Heaven with him. And she says it is a blessing I was spared, and a mercy and a providential escape and a warning.

So now I have told you all and you cannot think how much I cried. Because I do so long to be with you again. And the Fortescue children are to be buried in the churchyard to-morrow both together, but I am not to go. Aunt took me to see the grave this afternoon. It is full of rain-water and very deep and near the wall where I found the robin's nest with you last spring. So now good-bye. Please, dearest mother, write soon to me and come.

Your affectionate daughter,

DOROTHY.

P.S. I heard old Mrs. Helyar say to Aunt that Captain Beaumont is staying at the very same hotel as you are. If you ever see him, please say I have nearly done the pocket handkerchief I am doing for him.

NOCTURNE

Nocturne

(In Memory of Edgar Poe)

I OPENED the casement and looked into the
night.

All was still.

Then slowly there grew upon my ears a
confusion of faint moans. Every town, every
hamlet, every cottage gave forth sounds. They were
voices of children, of strong men and weak, of
righteous and unrighteous; and all cried out in
pain—cries of fear and agony and blasphemous
despair. And the voices grew louder until I could
understand not a few spoken words. They
lamented dismally among themselves in many
tongues:

"How I suffer! What have I done to deserve
this? Not a day of health—not a ray of hope!
Save me! Oh, the pain of it! I languish in chains!
Is this my reward? None so wretched as I! Ah,
why was I born? I have prayed in vain! Doomed
to long years of suffering—to a painful death!
Spare me! Kill me! Be merciful and kill me!
Kill!"

Said I to myself:

"This is the plaint of poor humanity, a plaint
such as might melt the Fiend to compassion."

And the voices grew yet louder and more piteous, a wail of bitterness, a discord of hideous shrieks that rang into the stillness, ear-piercing, heart-rending.

And I marvelled, and said:

" How comes it that I have hitherto been deaf to these distressful tones? "

Now, as I continued to hearken, a change crept over the universal plaint. For the howls and groans, the prayers and curses, ceased to sound in their separate manifestations, and the discords mingled like the strains of an Aeolian harp to form a symphony of tremendous chords, shrill and deep, that filled the air. As when the south wind, in furious gusts, breathes through the open reeds of some mighty organ till all is drowned in a seething ocean of melody: even so this torrent of suffering poured out upon the night—it swelled, sank low and swelled again, and never wholly ceased.

Passing wonderful! For lo! It was the old familiar song that had sung in my ears since the day of my birth, and into whose origin it had never been given me to enquire. And now, as my ear grew conscious and once more accustomed to the throbbing harmonies, I found them, in truth, not altogether unpleasant.

Then I understood.

And I said:

" Doubtless there is some Lover of Vocal Music overhead; some Being who takes pleasure in this chant and has contrived it for his own delectation."

INTELLECTUAL NOMADISM

Intellectual Nomadism

I

EVERY now and then the torrents that seam the plateau regions of inner Algeria swell to a river and pour down from the mountains in a seething wave of destruction. So it happened in October 1904, when part of the French settlement of Aïn Sefra was overwhelmed by a flood of this kind.

One of the wrecked buildings was inhabited at that moment by Isabelle Eberhardt, a young lady journalist, Russian by race, Mohammedan by religion; and among its ruins were found certain of her manuscript notes which now form a considerable part of a posthumous volume entitled *Dans l'Ombre Chaude de l'Islam*. They were unearthed during the excavations which were undertaken with great care by Lieutenant Paris, and found to be disconnected and very much damaged from having lain for several weeks in the mud. In order to attach the pieces Monsieur Barrucand, her friend,

and editor of an Algerian newspaper, was obliged
to string them together by reflections borrowed from
her correspondence, from her papers and travel
notes. This was the sole method of reconstruction,
he says, whereby he could save from definite
interment these fragments of Saharan life which
had reached his hands.

It was a labour of love and well worth
performing. A critic has called Isabelle " the most
virile and sincere writer of Algeria," and if the
reader wants still more diversified and still more
vividly flashing pictures of North-African life than
are contained in this and its sister volume, *Notes
de Route*, it is hard to say where he will find them.

In her early years, under the charge of an old
grand-uncle at Geneva, she had been brought up
" absolutely as a boy." And now on horseback,
alone and disguised as an Arab youth, she traversed
the inner parts of Algeria and Tunisia from the
borders of Morocco to those of Tripoli. These
volumes are records of her journeyings, impressions
of scenery interspersed with tales of native life and
her own reflections; they unfold a vast and varied
panorama—crumbling cities through whose narrow
streets you stumble in the twilight amid piles of
foul refuse, calm Arab convent retreats where white-
robed marabouts glide about like ghosts, the busy
life of green oasis gardens; anon you are riding
under a fiery sun through some gorge of scintillating
rock or reposing a while with the eternal wanderers

in their black tents perched on a weltering desolation of sand dunes; every aspect of native life flits past your eye—the soldiery, merchants, womenfolk and humble labourers; they all disclose their joys and hopes and sufferings; you feel, after reading these pages, as if you had been gazing upon one of those glowing Oriental tapestries full of bold tints that yet harmonise in a miraculous fashion and suggest, rather than reveal, some simple underlying design.

What is it—this sense of fundamental simplicity pervading the whole? It is the character of Isabelle Eberhardt herself.

She possesses the first requisite of a writer: she is non-derivative—true to her nature. And her nature being essentially Russian, she can sympathise to an exceptional degree with the nomadic Arabs. For your Russian, unbeknown to himself, has still much of the nomad in him.

Where is a country vast as his with so few local dialects? Despite the inland passport system which has striven to fix the people to the glebe, the roving tendency of the masses has triumphed over severe winters, uninhabitable tracts, immense rivers; over those marshy wastes impracticable in spring and autumn. Some idea of the difficulty of internal communication may be gained from the fact that before a good road can be built a railway must first be laid down (on wood) for the transport of the necessary stones, in which a great part of

Russia is deficient. Peasants leave their homes on a pilgrimage to some distant shrine, and so great is their love of wandering that they continue to roam across country from one sanctuary to another, forgetful of their old life, and are often found dead by the roadside. Whole villages migrate about those endless steppes. The wealthier classes think nothing of going from Petrograd to Moscow on the pretext of buying a hat or a pair of gloves. The Government has taken advantage of these erratic habits and, by the introduction of zone tariffs, secures large profits. Russian railways are paying concerns.

Note their luggage. For a journey of a few hours they must carry cooking apparatus, samovars, pillows, towels, and a mass of household paraphernalia that might advantageously have been left at home. Railway stations resemble gipsy encampments; second-class inns are Oriental caravanserais. Hotel proprietors, aware of this propensity and knowing that the common folk insist upon using bedding, etc., to which they have been accustomed from childhood and which never leaves them, fail to provide many articles considered necessary elsewhere. The officials at the frontier stations have the greatest difficulty in dealing with all the heterogeneous encumbrances which poorer travellers insist upon taking with them, even for a week's visit, to some friend across the boundary.

In the streets you will see all but the upper

classes walking in the centre of the roadway, heedless of the furious driving; they still feel themselves on the wild steppe, and are oblivious of the fact that a city, with its pavement for foot-passengers, has grown up around them. The town houses, many of them, are not yet numbered on the European principle; they are called by the names of their actual or former proprietors " the house of So-and-So "—suggesting the old patriarchal abode. Within, they do not look as if they were ever intended to be permanently occupied. Nothing has been, or will be, long in its place; clocks are not going, doors are not shut—an instinctive recollection of a former breezy tent-life; there is a surprising lack of furniture, especially of the kind which the Anglo-Saxon requires for storing away clothes and " settling down." Russians never settle down. They have all something in common with that old prince in one of their novels; rooms are put to new uses, beds moved from this room to that, out of sheer restlessness and love of change. They will live for weeks in a chaotic confusion that could be remedied by half an hour's work, but are buoyed up by a dim conviction that soon the encampment must be broken up and the family moved elsewhere.

The truth is that, in their heart of hearts, Russians hate all occupations that tie them down to a particular spot. Landed proprietors easily transfer their affections from one place to another,

buying and selling estates in different corners of
the country, without regard or remembrance of that
which gave them birth. They lack the feeling for
home as a fixed and old-established topographical
point. We think of a particular house or village
where we were born and where we spent our
impressionable days of childhood; these regard
home purely as a social centre—they are at home
everywhere, so long as their family is about them.
So you will find them at Continental watering-
places, never alone, like the Englishman, but
moving about in tribes and batches. Nomads!
They have a fairly rich language, yet it contains no
equivalent for our word " home."

One might go on for ever with these examples.
One might refer to the samovar, which is not only
a queer machine for making tea, but a symbol as
well—the pivot of their social life and the tangible
justification of the nomadic family principle. For
the Russian paterfamilias is not like ours. He is
Governor *par excellence* of his family, the sheik of
his clan; its members belong to him body and soul.
Great families have little ones dependent on them,
exactly as among the Arabs, and the humblest
householder possesses this authority by common
consent. One might also recall the Russian's frank
hospitality and its resemblance to that of the nomad
Bedouin, his extraordinary disregard for the feeling
of privacy in domestic life, another relic of the
wanderers' open tents. . . .

This does not mean that Isabelle Eberhardt, for example, was gadding, across country all day long with a Gladstone bag slung over her shoulders. But it means that the nomad's definite but indefinable states of yearning and exaltation, the nostalgic note, are prominent in these volumes. She has what she calls the " goût de l'espace "— the " volupté profonde de la vie errante."

Which reminds me that the old adage about " let us eat and drink, for to-morrow, etc." applies particularly to nomadic people. Their every joy of life is uncertain, for at any moment the settlement may be dispersed and the delights, which to-day offers, indefinitely postponed. So the Russian, like the nomadic Magyar or Arab, imposes little restraint upon himself in the matter of " wine, women and song "; he seizes upon the joys of life with zest and almost theatrical exaggeration, and this, again, is reflected in his literature. But it may be said—it has been said—that this lack of restraint is rather the result of a harsh climate; that it is a protest on the part of humanity against the inclemency of physical surroundings; that mankind, to counteract sombre conditions of nature, will tend towards spiritual excesses. There may be some truth in the general argument. No doubt the hysterical Scandinavian lore bears traces of such violent changes of summer and winter, light and darkness, as are unknown " under the roof of blue Ionian weather." But the influence of environment has become a kind of *deus ex machina* that explains away all difficulties. In the present instance the relative immoderation of the Russians contrasts significantly with the steadiness to which a longer social stability has accustomed the equally boreal Finlanders; the idiosyncrasies of the dreamy and restless Arab are altogether absent in the plodding Berber peasant, although he has dwelt far longer in this glowing and fateful land of Africa.

No, it is a matter of race and not of soil; and so much for Isabelle's nomadism.

As to her intellectuality: open these volumes where you will and the fact thrusts itself upon you.

This is the way she sees things:

" Les passants sont rares.

" Parfois un fellah, poussant devant lui un petit âne disparaissant sous une charge de palmes qui frôlent les murs avec un bruissement métallique. L'homme marche, l'œil vague, le bâton sur l'épaule. tenu très droit, d'un geste hiératique comme on en voit aux personnages des bas-reliefs égyptiens. Il chante, pour lui tout seul, doucement, une vieille mélopée berbère; il échange quelques salam distraits avec les fantômes blancs immobiles le long des murs. Une vieille paraît, courbée sous une outre pesante. Assis ou à demi couchés sur les bancs de terre, les ksouriens berbères blancs, ou les kharatine, autochtones noirs, parlent sans hâte, se grisant d'ombre et d'immobilité longue."

And thus she feels them:

" Il fait bon s'endormir ainsi, n'importe où, à belle étoile, en sachant qu'on s'en ira le lendemain et qu'on ne reviendra sans doute jamais, que tout ce qui est ne durera pas . . . tandis que chantent les Bédouins, tandis que pleurent les djouak,[1] tandis que s'évapore et s'éteint, comme une flamme inutile, la pensée . . ."

Many of her sketches, such as " Meriema," the tale of the old woman who lost her wits through the death of her son, or the mysterious figure of the young flute-player among the mouldering palaces of Tunis, the " Pleurs d'Amandier " and at least twenty others, are original in the good sense of the word; they are both new and truthful. And they will bear close scrutiny. Take that little one on " Lézards," for instance; or, in the other volume, the bizarre " Joies Noires." Here is not only fine observation, but a pronounced personal cachet sustained by scholarship and love of letters; these things are more than clever studies thrown off in a happy moment; they are—in a small way, of course, —the product of an independent mind which has gauged the resources of language, mastering its intricacies, discriminating its beauties, and realising its limitations.

The translator may well despair of preserving their voluptuous aroma; it evaporates in his crucible.

---

[1] The pastoral reed of the Bedouins.

II

" J'ai toujours été simple," says Isabelle, " et dans cette simplicité j'ai trouvé des jouissances fortes." Nothing is more true if by simple she means limpid, homogeneous. Unlike that Russian stone, the Alexandrite, she shines with the same steady glow, view her in what light you will; there may be flaws, but they are not the flaws of other people; a welcome quality in an age which produces so many human creatures, and so many books, which are merely reflections. And her opinions have been formed in the only way in which opinions that are worth anything can be formed: by copious reading—not to learn but, as the English sage has put it, " to weigh and consider "—and by contact with actualities, with the shifting world of men and the wild places of nature. She has drawn deep breaths of life; she has suffered and pondered and pined in solitude:

" C'est la plus déshéritée de ce monde, une exilée sans foyer et sans patrie, une orpheline dénuée de tout, qui écrit ces lignes. Elles sont sincères et vraies."

And elsewhere:

" J'en arrive a cette conclusion, qu'il ne faut jamais chercher le bonheur. Il passe sur la route, mais toujours en sens inverse. . . .

"Quand mon cœur souffrait, il commencait à vivre."

These gropings and strivings of mind have given poignancy to her language and a touch of mellow humanity, the antithesis of that hard machine-made glitter, that supercilious juggling with the obvious, which is praised as "profundity" in some writers of her sex.

It will never do to underestimate her arduous journalistic training when, locked in her little room, she wrestled with her thoughts and words, for it was thus that she learnt to avoid the pitfalls that beset the writers of her own race more than those of any other—diffuseness, lack of concentrative grasp. Russians will tell you that the sight of hedges, so familiar to lovers of our landscape, is irksome to their notions of liberty. They like to survey an unimpeded vista; to revel in that all-pervading sense of spaciousness which haunts one like a melody and exhales from countries devoid of landmarks—from those dim plains over which the eye roams, vainly seeking some point of repose, some steeple-crowned hillock or a range of distant mountains. Dwellers in narrow and secluded villages are prone to think that the whole world is contained within the mountains that encircle them, whence the *smugness* of the Swiss. Conversely, those whose ancestors have been accustomed to wander over limitless spaces may be supposed to have acquired a wider vision, a more restless temperament. This is reflected in the conversation of Russians, for nothing is more difficult than to keep them from " wandering from the point," their thoughts flit airily from one subject to another with inexhaustible wealth of ideas. That is their social charm. It is reflected in their fiction with its note of experimentation and unconventionality, its joy of roving—Gorki: the typical nomad—in unexplored domains of the mind; and in their characteristic failing as historians or philosophers. They like a wide grasp of their subject; they reach out too far, and yet must perforce include it all. So one of my acquaintances, who has been engaged for a number of years on a history of his country's rule in Central Asia, has at last, he tells me, reached the period of—Cyrus. Many writers must have been lost to Russia through this recoil from the imagined dimensions of their task. It is not wilful prolixity so much as an irresistible hereditary straining after spaciousness and wide horizons.

There is none of this straining in Isabelle; she never sees too much at a time; she knows her own limitations and those of her theme. That journalistic schooling taught her to think rapidly and surely, to eliminate the trivial; she deletes remorselessly, as can be seen by a glance at the *Notes de Route* where some of the old variants are printed below the new text. She is forever dissatisfied and a believer in conscientious labour rather than in inspiration; a born writer, for the rest, and "irresistibly drawn towards the career of letters." "I write," she says, "because I like the process of literary creation; I write, as I love, because such is probably my destiny. And it is my sole true consolation."

Now whoever looks in these pages for photographic reproduction of desert life will be disappointed. There is mirage hanging about them; like all artists, she detects colours and shapes invisible to the common eye; or, again, she is deliberately blind; her pictures of this "Holy land of Africa" are distortions in the sense of Turner's landscapes: distortions, that is, till we have risen to her point of view and learned to know better. She well knows the uses of that focussing or intensifying faculty which constitutes much of the charm of writers as different as Balzac and George Borrow. In this land of "menacing monotony" the artistic mind dwells lovingly upon the minutiæ of human affairs, the result being a magnified visualisation. The Arabs of Isabelle are so vital and palpitating that your ordinary ones melt away like phantoms. Elsewhere we are reminded of the aerial butterfly-touch of Hearn; of Maeterlinck's love of pictured metaphor:

"Que j'aime la verdure exubérante et les troncs vivants, plissés d'une peau d'éléphant, de ces figuiers gonflés de lait amer, autour desquels bourdonnent des essaims de mouches dorées!"

K

And those abysmal desert silences, those spaces of tawny desolation over which the eye roams and vainly seeks a point of repose, often turned her thoughts inwards and invested her, as they do the Arabs, with their dream states.

" Oh ! la bienheureuse annihilation du moi, dans cette vie contemplative du désert ! . . . Parfois cependant il est encore de ces heures troublées où l'esprit et la conscience, je ne sais pourquoi, se réveillent de leur longue somnolence et nous torturent. . . .

" Combien de fois n'ai-je pas senti mon cœur se serrer en songeant à ma vocation d'écrire et de penser, à mon ancien amour de l'étude et des livres, à mes curiosités intellectuelles de jadis. . . . Heures de remords, d'angoisse et de deuil. Mais ces sentiments n'ont presque jamais d'action sur la volonté qui reste inerte et n'agit point."

Herein lies the justification of that subjective method which she handles so craftily.

An interesting phenomenon in literature, this modern taste for personalities, fostered, as it may well have been, by the interviewer who has accustomed us to pry into the most intimate details of our neighbours' private lives. Certain it is that the position of a descriptive writer towards his public has undergone a change of late; readers have become anthropomorphous, connoisseurs of sensations; they commune with an author not only for what he writes, but for what he is; they endeavour to spy into the windows of his soul and to overhear him chronicling his most casual moods and impressions. They want to learn how things affect him. And there is a contagion in wisely premeditated indiscretions and *asides* on the part of an author, for we are all creatures of impulse, liable to unguarded moments, and from sharing his feelings we may be led to adopt his views; to gain, that is, some definite acquisition of knowledge. But whoever is not constitutionally honest had better remain impersonal. In other words, the chronicling of moods depends upon whose moods they are. Those of Isabelle Eberhardt are sincere and interesting.

Apart from that catholicity of hers which transports us with equal ease through such varied phases of African existence, one point must strike every careful reader: her sense of propriety in regard to the length of these sketches. That there are picturesque vignettes in the scenery of life which look best in the microscopic setting of a sonnet or even an epigram; that fleeting emotions will befit the prose poem, compact entities the short tale, while whoever wishes to delineate the teeming markets of mankind and mountains and meandering streams and all the orographical and hydrographical complexities of continents must call for the Gargantuan canvas of *Anna Karenina*: these are surely obvious rules. But how often are they violated, even by writers of reputation! Her pieces, however, have frames suitable to their size; some, like the " Petit Monde de Femmes," are the veriest miniatures, while the mournful " Fellah " trails its sad length along, a monotone of " misery, falling drop by drop "; a kind of literary bas-relief. Short or long, they read so uncommonly easily that their technique will repay study as illustrating the remark of Sheridan to a lady: " Easy reading, Madam, is damned hard writing." And throughout it all we are never without an exhilarating sense of motion; the camels are groaning, the tents must be struck. This is what takes away from these sketches the air of a set purpose and invests them with an impromptu charm.

This is far from saying that her pages contain the final word of such literature, since what fulfils the needs of to-day is sure to be found inadequate for the morrow. So it is with this feeling for the desert. The Sahara used to exist only in its terrifying aspects of desolation and heat and thirst. Then came a generation of men who discovered for us its manifold beauties; this, we said, was the truth and the whole truth, at last: the desert as a mode of art! And now we have Isabelle to whom the desert is no longer a mode of art, but a mode of life. (The Alps have passed through the same three stages.)

She is merged into these sand-wastes and their rude activities not by æsthetic intuition, but by identity of temperament.   Unity of race, religion and language is a powerful national bond, but the peculiarity of the Russians as a people is that of the Arabs; it lies in a sentiment of brotherhood, a kind of apostolic spirit, that binds together the highest and lowest in the land and has its roots in their patriarchal institutions.   You will notice in many of their writers a full-blooded, *warming element* in which those of industrial countries— America, for instance — are wholly deficient. Isabelle, Arab and Russian, has broad fraternal feeling—" We are all poor devils," she says, " and they who refuse to understand us are poorer than ourselves."   She knows a test for revealing the virtue that lurks in the breast of the meanest human creature, the test of her own worthlessness; she would even find it possible to say a good word for those savages of Albion who vulgarise desert life by establishing decent roads and communications whereby emotional travellers, prancing over the wilderness in sumptuous seed-pearl embroidered dressing-gowns, may jot down its beauties for readers of the *Figaro* without having their throats cut.   Like Loti, by the way, she has grasped the peculiar colour-value of harsh scientific or commercial words.   How, in a flow of purely literary speech, they hold the eye—these crude importations from an alien realm of thought!   They seem to complete the picture; they are the poppies in a field of wheat.

But what will strike the reader as her dominant note, besides a non-derivative outlook, is that sense of measure, the more to be admired in a young woman who knew so much of her subject, who felt so keenly and could wield so fluent a pen. Remembering that these sketches were written for a provincial newspaper, one appreciates still more highly her conscientious work.

Nevertheless, a man who should profess to be able to imagine nothing better than these descriptions of Isabelle's would only prove that he had reached the limit of his powers of assimilation. So it is. We grow tired of the strain of novelty—for it is a strain; we sometimes even cast off as too exhausting our most recent author friends and revert to those of our youth in whom we affect to discover beauties hitherto unrevealed, thus making a virtue of a physiological necessity, weariness. Her work is of the kind that can only be done once satisfactorily; the perusal of her imitators or disciples, of whom there are three or four on the French literary market just now, illustrates sufficiently the difference between reality and its shadow. It is difficult, indeed, to conceive another writer emerging upon the scene with the unusual equipment she possessed : to be both man and woman, Asiatic and European, a scholar and a savage of the waste, a visionary hashish devotee and fin-de-siècle journalist; a Mohammedan, Christian and agnostic.

Yes; another generation may well find her too

personal (for we shall soon be outgrowing the anthropomorphous stage once more) and perhaps also too flutteringly restless. Carlyle somewhere says that the nomad lacks the " tendency to persevere." Very true : they only sow who care to wait for the harvest. There is Oudjda, for instance, that sombre city of putrefaction and death which grows fair only after sunset when, as in a dream, one hears the Aissouyiahs praying "dans la sérénité pudique de la nuit, voilant la pourriture des choses, la souffrance et l'abjection des êtres:" how one longs, after reading those few pages, to know more about such a place as this, to live oneself into it! But—no. With the swiftness of doom the scenery is shifted and " *c'est la fin. Le somptueux rideau vert et argent des oliviers s'est renfermé sur toutes ces courtes visions.*"

For the rest, it is always easy to discover defects in our favourites, once we have grown tired of them.

A new edition might profitably give translations of the many Arabic words which bristle in this one : what does the ordinary European know of *souafa, guira, djemaa, hamada, harair, djellaba, ihram, mhlahfa, taleb, sehan, zeriba, cagna, houma, targui, toubib* and the rest of them? This is rather an ultra-virile method of introducing local colour.

III

" *J'ai toujours été simple. . . .*"

That was likewise the conviction of Marie
Bashkirtseff who, despite her different fortune,
resembles Isabelle in her aspirations: to escape
from a world of sordid trivialities, to leave a mark.
And highly must we rate these children of the
North who found unaided the true remedy for those
brooding states that clog the mind and warp the
character in—activities. Marie, one remembers,
was everlastingly " in a fever to study."

True, they possessed the advantage of belong-
ing to a race which has not undergone the schooling
of the rest of Europe, which knows nothing
of Reformation or Renaissance, which has not
obfuscated its mind with metaphysics, classical
ideals and " *Sturm-und-Drang* "; which is enabled.
therefore, to graft the latest fruits of modern
knowledge upon a sound barbarian stock. All this
has its drawbacks, no doubt. Ignorant and even
scornful of Hellenic traditions, their mundane art
lacks the element of repose and concentrative
thought; Russian Church art languishes in ancient
conventional grooves and displays nothing of that
persistent and active regard for beauty which has
culminated in the dome of St. Peter or the
Madonnas of Raphael. But in literature and

speculative thought the profit is largely on their side, for they have not been told during long centuries what to see on earth and how to see it. They are not loaded down with traditions and precedents which are no longer mentors but simply milestones along the road of learning, milestones that we non-Russians ought to leave respectfully behind us, instead of taking them up on our shoulders and staggering along while they sit there like the Old Man of the Sea. Only think: never to have vexed one's soul with Plato and Cimabue and Categorical Imperatives. and the thousand other "essentials" of Western culture—what would one not give to feel really Russian for half an hour! Then, and only then, might one grasp the full charm of the *anti-parochial* spirit that pervades all Russian life and literature; a spirit such as you will vainly seek, for instance, in France which, for all its civilisation, is the most parochial country on earth. This anti-parochialism is a feature in the writings of both Marie and Isabelle; it gives to both of them an elevating, aristocratic note.

Yet Isabelle, like many artists of natural nobility, is a democrat:

"On m'a souvent reproché de me plaire avec les gens du peuple. Mais où donc est la vie, sinon dans le peuple? Partout ailleurs le monde me semble étroit. . . . A vrai dire, je ne souffre pas trop des pauvretés et des naïvetés, pas même des grossièretés. Je n'en souffre pas profondément."

For purposes of insight into a race like the Arabs the advantages of being a woman are twofold; she has not only access into their veiled and intimate life, but also is less disposed to theorise, to read wrong meanings into what she sees, less prone to err in interpreting primordial traits of feeling—less introspective, in short. A man can rarely immerse himself in the life of a savage race with the naïf abandonment of a woman. And if he can, he is a savage himself, unable to communicate his experiences to others; there is not enough of the child and barbarian left in him; he is no longer permeable, having donned too many garments of culture in the past. As a writer and observer he may do something better in his way, but the spirit of freemasonry with an alien stock which comes naturally to a woman like Laurence Hope would argue, in a man, a quite exceptional detachment. " J'ai voulu posséder ce pays," says Isabelle, " et ce pays m'a possédée."

" Ce pays m'a possédée : " there you have it.

This elective affinity of some women for wild and destructive races of mankind—is it that their development has been arrested at the emotional stage when, as children, we were wont to delight in pirate adventures and redskin-scalpings, or because, seriously reflecting, they think to discover in this return to barbarism a remedy for the self-questionings and the social complexities of modern days? Whatever be the reason, a man will not so often have these " jouissances fortes "—a term under which we are to understand a throbbing sympathy with everything, good or bad, that the country or its people offers.

Isabelle's philosophy, like that of Marie Bashkirtseff, is summed up in a determination to keep every pore open, and it is worth remarking that both of them stand ethically, as they do geographically, midway between East and West. They are Occidental in their enjoyment of novelty and strenuous labour, but sufficiently Buddhistic to despise the delirious bustle and herd-spirit of our civilisation; to detest every form of Western hypocrisy.

In matters pertaining to the sexes Isabelle has the cynicism of the Oriental. These volumes of hers contain some pages not exactly fitted for the young person but, on the whole, they are pervaded by a refreshing sanity.

She says, for example:

" L'amour le plus décevant et le plus pernicieux me semble être surtout la tendance occidentale vers l'âme-sœur. . . . Gloire à ceux qui vont seuls dans la vie! Si malheureux qu'ils soient, ce sont les forts et les saints, les seuls êtres. Les autres ne sont que des moitiés d'âme."

Was ever a truth, a fine Crim-Tartary truth, more plainly enunciated?

It may be asked what reflections such as this have to do with a description of the Tunisian desert?

Simply this: they are the outcome of a mood created by local conditions, and in so far help us to understand them. Here, face to face with infinities, man disencumbers himself; he casts off outworn weeds of thought and feeling; he stands alone; he must act; he cannot be bothered with a sister-soul; the caravan is waiting to begin the march, and at night, after a meagre repast, he will drop from sheer physical fatigue into a dreamless sleep. An anodyne for many ills. . . .

In their revolt against every form of crooked emotionalism these Russian girls have struck a new note, and the right one. There is a charming chapter in the " Ombre de l'Islam " where Isabelle describes supper-time at the Mellah, the Jew quarter; its stench, its vulgarity, its " bonheur facile."

" Je connais très bien leur âme: elle monte dans les vapeurs de la marmite. . . . Je les envie d'être ainsi. Ils sont la critique de mon romanticisme et de cet incurable malaise que j'ai apporté du Nord et de l'Orient mystique avec le sang de ceux qui ont vagabondé avant moi dans la steppe. . . .

" Loin de moi les tâtonnements de mon adolescence maladive! . . . Toute mon éducation morale est à refaire."

In the face of such self-criticism, how absurd to call her " neurotic ": as if it were not a symptom of uncommon healthfulness to be able to review oneself in this objective fashion. It would be more correct to say that Isabelle has taken the gold of

the romantic movement and discarded its dross—
the slobbering cant, the sentimentality. Her sound
barbaric ethics are untainted by the virus of
prurience; her whole religion resumes itself into a
rather spasmodic, sisterly hankering after an honest
God, a kind of blandly-beaming *bon vieux* such as
Lucretius had in mind.

Marie Bashkirtseff was an anti-sentimentalist of
the same type—her attitude towards the male sex
was one of playful sanity. The good Mathilde
Blind used to regret that Marie had not lived long
enough to meet her " ideal." The fact seems to be
that these Russian girls are seldom on the lookout
for ideals. And it is rather instructive to observe
that they often find something less vaporous, something that wears better. How does it come about?
Can it be that, although they are in one sense " New
Women," they nevertheless belong to a variety
different from the odd compound of childishness
and ferocity which goes by that name—to a class
of female with whom a man discovers rational
companionship to be not altogether out of the
question?

Isabelle tried the experiment and found it a
success.   In the year 1900, at the age of twenty-
three, she married according to the Mohammedan
rites a native officer, naturalised Frenchman, to
whom she was much attached (like many of her sex,
she always had a weakness for the soldiery).

And there occurred next year an unpleasant episode. While near Eloued she was attacked by a religious fanatic who belonged to a confraternity hostile to hers and so severely wounded that she lay for a month in the military hospital of that town. This was followed by an order for her expulsion from Algerian territory for " political reasons "— an order only applicable as against non-Frenchmen (she was still an alien, the authorities having forbidden the pair to make their religious union valid by a civil marriage). Vainly she applied to the Russian Consulate to learn the reason of this step. She had been accused ere this of anti-French propaganda, a charge she vehemently denied; they had even gone so far as to suspect her of being an English Methodist in disguise. Isabelle Eberhardt a Methodist! Truly a wondrous juxtaposition of ideas. But the French are a wondrous nation; their pathological suspiciousness of the outsider reminds one of those old Athenians. By no effort of will-power or imagination can they put themselves into the mental condition of another race; it is an odd little weakness of theirs; impossible to believe the depths of credulity to which this *idée fixe* sometimes leads them. Foreigners suffer, for there are moments when the most innocuous of them objects to living in the publicity of Le Roi Soleil; when those concierge reports, those genteel but persistent questionings, that police dossier which dogs his footsteps, be he in African deserts or in the heart of Paris, make him wish that this great modern nation were not quite so small-minded.[1]

In exile at Marseilles, separated from husband, without money and still suffering from the effects of her wound, a hard life began; such was her necessity that she was obliged to work with Italian dock-hands of the port; instead of cigarettes she smoked sycamore leaves. But presently the husband contrived to exchange into another regiment which brought him to Marseilles; here they were remarried according to French law, and Isabelle, now following the domicile of her husband, became a French citizen and returned to Algeria in spite of her proscription.

They seem to have established their headquarters at the little cantonment of Aïn Sefra which she has so well described, and to have lived there happily till the day when the house was invaded by cataracts of slime brought down in that flood of October 1904.

It cost Isabelle her life.

" I can swim," she told him. " I will hold you up."

She was trying to patch together some kind of raft when the masonry suddenly yielded to the pressure of the waters and fell upon her, the husband

[1] Georges Clarétie relates how he once accompanied the Contrôlleur of Tozeur on a delicate official pursuit after English lady Methodists who, disguised as natives, had been making a dangerous anti-French propaganda among the Arabs. They found nothing; the desert, he says, " kept its secret."

escaping by a miracle. They recovered her body two days later and entombed it in the native cemetery on the bleak hillside, near some crumbling maraboutic shrine. There she lies in the desert sand, and her head is turned towards the East.

Twenty-seven years. It was a short life, but she pressed the grape to the last drop.

From where these lines have been written, at Nefta on the borders of the Sahara, the eye can follow the track which leads across the burning salt waste of the Chott to Eloued, her elected home. It gives a pungency to these pages of hers, and one shapes in fancy some picture of the tall Arab youth, with the childlike smile, riding yonder on that much-beloved white Soufi stallion.

" *Je ne me suis pas composée un ideal; j'ai marché à la découverte.*" That is the key-note of her life.

And one remembers that other intellectual nomad Marie Bashkirtseff, who died yet younger; who also found a " *frisson intérieur* " necessary to her " *hygiène morale*"; who was likewise for ever learning and marching to the discovery of new horizons. For a mental state such as theirs, appetency rather than instability is the right word. Their writings are neither of the kind to which we go for information, nor of the purely æsthetic species; they belong to the category of confessions or mirrors of the soul; human documents, to use Mallock's happy phrase, that disclose the rainbow-tinted world as it filters through the medium of a single candid intelligence. To call them creative artists would be a mistake. They are women of keen and yet disciplined impressionability, accessible to every generous impulse and, in so far, a delectable offshoot from the common trend of feminism.

L

THE LAST WORD

The Last Word

(In memory of Maupassant)

IT was in the depth of winter, many long years ago. We were sitting up, a party of four, round an immense fire at the country-house of my brother-in-law Edmond in Central France. The new arrival of that morning was the then Minister of Justice, Monsieur Henri de B——, a connection of our host and a pleasant man of undoubted ability, whose independent action in the notorious and complicated Trémont case has been deservedly praised. I had never met him before; indeed, it was the first time he ever visited the district. A prodigious wolf-hunt was already organised for the next day—weather permitting—in honour of his coming.

The conversation turned upon the catastrophe of the Tay Bridge in Scotland, a lamentable disaster that will be fresh, no doubt, in the memory of the older generation.

" Horrible, horrible," said our host, my brother-in-law. " It is difficult to conceive any form of death more harrowing."

165

The Minister remarked:

" I can conceive more distressful accidents."

" Doubly horrible," added our other guest, a retired army surgeon, " occurring, as it did, in the pitch-black night, in that howling tempest—"

" On the contrary, monsieur, I venture to think we must regard that as an alleviating circumstance."

Our host said:

" I believe you are right, Henri. I was once eye-witness of an accident that seemed to me far more horrible on that very account. I happened to be walking one cloudless afternoon along the path that runs at the edge of the Rhinefall at Schaff-hausen. Imagine my surprise on seeing, not far away, a boat containing a party of ladies and gentlemen, visitors at my hotel, and with whom I had already exchanged a few words of civility. I called to warn them of the evident danger, but although they must surely have heard me, they seemed to be entirely occupied with their rowing. Then the truth dawned upon me. They were already caught in the terrific current, and the men strained every nerve to row up stream again. It was too late. Too late! Ah, my dear Henri, what a sickening spectacle! Those two or three minutes were prolonged to an eternity. As the boat approached the fatal edge it was drawn forward with inconceivable rapidity. Then the men suddenly dropped their oars, and a scream came from that boat —a scream such as I hope never to hear again. It leapt like lightning over the edge, and I saw nothing but a confused mass of brightly-coloured dresses mingling with the rainbows and mists that rose up to meet them from the steaming abyss. Not a particle of them was ever found; they must have been torn to shreds. A horrible death! When one thinks of those happy young people within a stone's throw of land, the glorious sun shining over-head. . . ."

"Horrible, yes," replied the Minister. "Your illustration is, from the point of view of the horrible, doubtless an improvement in various ways upon the Scotch catastrophe. But there are yet worse deaths. There are ignoble deaths. Let me explain myself. I use that word as opposed to noble. Ignoble deaths are always horrible, and sometimes more. This was a horrible death; it was not an ignoble one."

"A fine distinction," said the doctor. "Besides," he added, "it was merciful, inasmuch as it was sudden. These poisonings by prussic acid, these fallings into vats of melted sugar or agricultural machines are all quick deaths. What are two or three minutes? On the other hand a lingering fatal disease is too long—the sufferer enjoys a respite, an interval of forgetfulness, of hope."

"You are an ogre," I said.

"A harmless one," added my brother-in-law, "like all military men."

"I agree with you, monsieur," said the Minister.

" A particle of hope, a momentary release from pain, destroys what one might call the artistic effect."

We all laughed. It was characteristic of the man to throw his whole soul into a subject—into any subject that happened to crop up. I observed:

" Your Excellency is not easily satisfied. Let me suggest, as the high-water mark of ignoble deaths, the possibility of being buried alive. Would you not call it the Last Word? For in this instance, you will admit, we pass a sufficiently disagreeable quarter of an hour, an uninterrupted agony of body and mind, a sensation of utter hopelessness—"

" Well, yes—perhaps," mused the Minister. " Yet I think the agony might, under circumstances, be protracted still further. It is such an important element, you see, that duration of time. In a coffin the air would soon be exhausted, I suppose. Let me see: how many square feet. . . ." It was interesting to note what fine points he raised while dilating upon the gruesome theme. " And then, sir —since we appear to have settled down to discuss this unpleasant subject—I think that a premature burial is not, for another reason, entirely satisfactory. It does not exhaust the full capabilities of suffering. Why? For the simple reason that there is something worse than this sheer hopelessness of which you speak. There is something incomparably worse. I fancy there must be cases on record in which the victim, while realising the hopelessness

of his position, is tormented in addition by the
knowledge that friends are close at hand, eager to
help if they but knew of his plight. Would you
not regard that as an aggravation, an æsthetic
refinement?"

"Certainly. It is a point of view which has
never struck me before. And I think I could cite
a case in illustration. I lately read of a shoemaker
—one of a large party—who accidentally slipped
into the crater of Mount Vesuvius and was
suspended head downwards at a great depth by
his coat, which had miraculously caught on a
projecting rock. He hung over the awful cauldron
not daring to move or even call out, for fear of
shaking himself free, besides dreading every minute
to lose consciousness in the sulphur fumes and drop
down. His friends on the height shouted to him,
but he dared not answer. At last they went away.
Perhaps they thought him dead. Imagine his
feelings."

"Nevertheless," he objected, "he may have
been buoyed up by some shadow of hope, however
faint. And that would impair the perfect harmony."

"He was saved in the end, after hanging there
for two or three days."

"He was saved!" He said it in a tone of
bitter disappointment. "That ruins the situation.
Besides—an agony of three days! That is too
long. I consider twelve hours a substantial
measure."

"You reason like a Grand Inquisitor."

The doctor added with enthusiasm:

"His Excellency speaks like a true artist and connoisseur."

The doctor resumed the subject:

"Allow me to subject to Your Excellency's consideration the following example, which I trust may meet with your approval. Some fifteen years ago I was invited, at Saint Etienne, to view unprofessionally the remains of a stoker who had met with an unusual fate. It seems that the poor wretch had climbed, presumably for the sake of coolness—it was in the heat of summer—into some part of an immense unfinished furnace. He fell asleep there, and during this interval the entrance was bricked up and the fire lighted. It was only next day that his absence was remarked and the furnace opened—an expensive piece of work—at the suggestion of one of his companions, who remembered having seen the unhappy man creep in. The workmen all agreed in stating that they had heard unnatural roarings in the furnace, which died away as the fire grew hotter."

"I congratulate you, my friend," I said. "That last stroke, especially, was masterful."

"You have brought us a good step forward, monsieur," remarked the Minister. "And I am particularly thankful to you for this illustration, as it supports my previous contention. For this is decidedly a more ignoble form of death than a

premature burial, in so far as it is even less natural
and less decorous; and, in addition, I cannot but
think that the agony was prolonged to more than
that bad quarter of an hour of which we spoke.
Only imagine—a large, roomy furnace as opposed
to a narrow coffin! And then, that delicate
embellishment: the proximity of friends! Only a
foot of brick and mortar between life and death.
. . . Yes, we are narrowing the sphere. And yet,
from an artistic point of view, this case leaves much
to be desired. It is by no means the Last Word on
the subject of the ignoble. It suffers, in my
opinion, from a radical defect."

" A defect? " we all asked.

He replied:

" The ignoble surely becomes intensified in
proportion as it afflicts those who are not ignoble.
What is a shoemaker? A stoker? Ignoble
personages. The quality must be brought into
sharper relief; to the bodily suffering there must be
superadded a mental and moral agony such as we
cannot suppose ignoble persons to appreciate.
For, let us freely confess, they are like men of
another nation in this, that their torments and griefs
do not appeal to us as keenly as do those of our own
social class."

" The impalement of ten thousand Chinamen
leaves me cool," interjected the doctor.

" Very true, monsieur. But I was referring
exclusively to accidental deaths, for to the ignoble

ones devised by man against man there is, I fear, no imaginable limit. And I was saying that the sufferings of vulgar people are rarely interesting. The great dramatists of all ages knew why they selected well-born personages to suffer a tragic or noble fate, and a certain Teutonic thinker has correctly explained the matter when he says that they fall from a greater height than the common herd. The same applies to ignoble fates. Tragic deaths move our tears, ignoble ones our disgust; and I presume the extreme of either is reserved for the aristocracy. Now it is precisely the extreme of the ignoble—in this particular department—which we are seeking to attain; that point beyond which there is nothing more ignoble. Therefore I say that, for the ignoblest death, the subject must be of noblest race and noblest mind. He cannot be too carefully chosen!"

"I mark and appreciate Your Excellency's qualification," observed the doctor. "I should suggest further, as regards the age of the subject, that he should be young. That seems appropriate."

"There is doubtless something more outrageous, something more revolting to our sense of fitness and of beauty, in the death of a young person than in that of one who has already taken his fill of years. Yet I venture to disagree with you. To my way of thinking, youth is invariably deficient in dignity and repose, two qualities—perhaps only extrinsic ones—that figure in our conception of what is truly noble. The full-blooded generosity of youth may shine in tragical situations, but it does not offer such an antithesis to the *ignoble* as the calm and almost sacred dignity of age, the violation of which is ignoble in a peculiar degree. No! I am disposed to think that the subject should be well stricken in years."

" Let me add another restriction," I added. " It should be a woman. There is a pathos in the relative weakness and refinement of the sex—"

" By all means, sir. It should be a woman. We are now approaching the climax, for it only remains to decide upon the agency of her death, and the manner. It should above all things be as unnatural, as degrading, as possible, for the essence of the ignoble is that which debases the dignity of man, even as the tragic exalts it. . . . Our host is thoughtful. Well, Edmond, you have not uttered a syllable for some time past. Are you about to make a suggestion? "

" Strangely enough," said my brother-in-law, " I could relate from my own experience a case that fulfils, I think, every one of the various conditions of the ignoble which you have deduced, one after the other, with so much logic and sagacity, and by the help of such edifying examples. In fact, if I may say so, it goes beyond your ideal; it improves upon it. I should call it positively the Last Word."

" The Last Word! "

" Ah! "

" It concerns an old lady who lived, when I was still a little boy, in a two-roomed cottage on this very estate. She was popularly known as the Duchess from the great airs she gave herself, but my mother told me her correct name was la Marnière, or something like that. She was of noble blood but poor; poor as a rat, and a chronic sufferer from rheumatism. She lived alone with an enormous family of cats, ten or fifteen of them, in whose company she seemed to take the greatest pleasure, perhaps because they were the only remaining friends who would deign to share her lot and not make poverty a subject of reproach. As to her character, everybody was agreed that she was gracious and full of charm, and that she bore her bitter fate with composure. My mother, I know, took sincere delight in her company. She made pitiable efforts to disguise her destitution; nothing, I imagine, can be more irksome than poverty to a fastidious female mind, nothing more calculated to undermine the sense of dignity."

" Very true," we agreed.

" I have no doubt that, while my sainted parent yet lived, she continued in passably good circumstances, for her pride never disdained to accept help from a friend of her own sex and whom she considered as of her own standing. I well remember those periodical visits to the cottage and the impression of penury they made upon me as a child. Everything was cramped and mean; doubly so, when I heard her discoursing in an affected language, and of matters I did not understand. To revenge myself, I used to tease her cats. They sat about the room, sleek and mysterious, occupied with their own thoughts. Poor as she was, she used to deny herself food in order to keep them alive, and gave to each one of them the name of some royal or exalted personage. That struck me, I remember, as peculiarly laughable."

" Such cases are not rare," observed the doctor.

" Common enough, I daresay. My mother told me never to laugh at her, but to respect her age and poverty. Sometimes she added that the old lady was a distant connection of our own family whose pride prevented her from appearing as such. I imagined at first that this was only said to heighten my reverence, but my mother assured me it was neither more nor less than the truth, and if so—why then, my dear Henri," turning to the Minister, " she may have been a connection of yours as well! Meanwhile it made me laugh yet more ; it struck me as a very ludicrous idea. And I am sorry to say that after my mother's sudden death the affairs of our poor relation went from bad to worse. She fell into the direst want—such want as we can scarcely believe to exist. Often she had nothing but a crust of bread for dinner. She was clothed in rags, and suffered terrible hardships, the cats, of course, suffering proportionately. And, in addition to her poverty, the torments of rheumatism increased to such an extent that she spent long periods on her wretched couch, unable to move. I need hardly say that I discovered all this only when it was too late. For soon after my bereavement I left for Paris and thence, as you know, for the East. I wrote from Paris to the Charity Sisters and to several other ladies, interesting them on her behalf. But her unreasoning pride did not simplify matters. For the rest, these excellent persons seem to have forgotten my recommendations very quickly. I am told that one of her latest fancies was that she professed to be afraid of being robbed and murdered on account of her diamonds; she would lock herself in her room for weeks at a time. Laughable, and yet sad. When I returned from my voyage, she was no longer living. A neighbour had broken into the cottage and found her dead. There was not much to bury, from all accounts."

" How so? "

" What do you mean, Edmond? "

" The cats, you understand. Maddened, I suppose, by hunger and thirst, they devoured her as she lay there helpless to move a finger; devoured her alive. An inconceivably hideous death, and all too slow into the bargain! Now tell me: would you not call that the Last Word? "

We were silent for a few moments, each of us doubtless endeavouring to conjure up in his own mind some picture of that appalling final scene. Then the doctor began judicially:

" The Last Word? I am not certain. Let us

suppose that, instead of one, there had been two of these poor old ladies, each equally crippled and suffering within sight of the other. The ignoble effect would clearly have been heightened. Therefore, alas! it is not the Last Word. Suppose there had been three, or four, or a hundred—"

" Insatiable monster! "

The Minister replied:

" I think, sir, that, from the point of view of the ignoble, the effect would not have been heightened." Then he added, with that cold intellectual discrimination which he had displayed throughout the evening: " It seems to me that wherever we encounter intelligent spectators, even though they be fellow-sufferers, the tragic element intervenes. And where it intervenes, it dominates. For my part," he concluded, " I consider that we have well-nigh exhausted the subject."

Then, having said these words, he stood up from his chair and suddenly raised his hand to his brow, as though he had remembered something. I glanced at him. He looked unaccountably perturbed, and soon began striding up and down the room harassed, as it seemed, by some troublesome thought.

" Yes," I agreed. " I think we have nearly reached the climax."

" Nearly," echoed the doctor in a somewhat dissatisfied tone. He was apparently still waiting for the Last Word.

The Last Word was soon to come.

M

Meanwhile our host summed up the discussion.

"Evidently," he said, "there is in human nature an uncharitable ingredient which takes pleasure in contemplating, or at least discoursing upon, the sufferings of our fellow-creatures. It is useless to deny this fact. The tiger-ancestry, maybe. Any ordinary person, listening to our conversation to-night, would have said we were a pack of blood-thirsty vampires; whereas, in point of fact, we are four quite exemplary and decent-minded citizens, are we not? . . . Let us go on to the balcony and examine the sky."

We rose at his suggestion and stepped out. It was bitterly cold. The thermometer had fallen to many degrees below freezing-point. The air was exhilarating and pure, and we walked up and down for a while in silence. Another spirit had fallen upon us. His Excellency alone seemed agitated in a remarkable degree. ("My God!" I heard him say to himself.) I wondered what he had found to disquiet his mind so suddenly and so intensely.

The doctor remarked to me:

"In the plenitude of life, how glibly one talks of death! The sights that I have seen! The words that I, unwillingly, have heard! I was present, my friend, on the field of Solferino."

But the Minister, now trembling with emotion, turned to my brother-in-law and asked in a low voice:

"The old lady of whom you spoke, the so-called

Duchess—was it by chance a Mademoiselle Hélène de la Marlinière?"

"How odd that you should know better than I do! Yes; that was her correct name. I remember it perfectly now."

"She left Paris in the late thirties?"

"So I understand. She left it in order to escape the persecutions of her relatives; she hid herself so well down here, in the provinces, that they never discovered her whereabouts, and this little triumph gave her pleasure. They had treated her as little short of a disgrace to the family. It is infamous."

"Ah! Because she refused to marry a rich old banker called Vilbort?"

"I have heard something to that effect. I see, my dear Henri, that you are acquainted with the matter. Perhaps in your official capacity—"

"My God! She was the only sister of my mother. . . ."

We looked into the night. The Park, with its solemn avenues, lay at our feet embedded in snow. Beyond, stretched a vast expanse of undulating forest country. The young moon had already gone to rest, but the snow, between sombre patches of shadow, glittered tremulously with the reflected scintillations of a myriad stars. There was a stillness in the atmosphere, a boreal calm, that promised good sport for next morning.

A MAD ENGLISHMAN

A Mad Englishman

I HAVE been learning about the Ass Wouralia;
likewise about the Rumpless Fowl and its
absurd and unnatural objection to laying
fertile eggs; about the Vulture's Nose, and Apple
Trees, and Cannibalism and Dry Rot; about Tight
Shoes, Tight Stays, and Tight Cravats. In other
words, needless to say, I have been reading Charles
Waterton's Essays on Natural History—magnificent
stuff! Or rather, re-reading them. For a close
inspection of the dusty volumes has revealed an
inscription to the effect that they were purchased by
myself in the summer of 1882; and the pages,
furthermore, are enriched with holograph annota-
tions of that year, setting forth very candidly my
opinion of the author and his work. It has given
me mixed feelings to peruse this running commentary, testifying, as it does, to a dreadfully
deficient sense of humanity, to considerable love
of natural history coupled with a certain elvish
facetiousness which may well have passed, in those
unregenerate days, for humour. How odd they
are—these glimpses into one's own vanished self!

Of course we all know Waterton's *Wander-*

ings—that astounding book wherein, by the help of copious tags from Horace and Cervantes, the *courteous reader* is beguiled from his comfortable fireside into the wilds of Guiana, there to undergo nerve-shattering encounters with Labari snakes and other improbable monsters, to devour monkey-flesh and ride on crocodiles. Let me at once say that I firmly believe this crocodile business. Nobody, you will argue, has ever ridden on a cayman. Exactly! Nobody but Waterton would have dreamt of doing any of the things he did. Nobody, for example, would dream of riding on a crocodile. That settles it. Waterton rode on a crocodile.

One would think that a naturalist penetrates into these tropical jungles in order to study their wonderful life or to collect birds and insects. But such is not his style : not a bit of it. He goes there to find the Wourali poison, being convinced—for some cryptic reasons which I despair of elucidating—that it might prove a cure for hydrophobia. And why should a non-professional trouble his head about the treatment of hydrophobia? Ah, that is Waterton's secret and his charm! Why, indeed—why any of the funny things he did?

It is a pity that we possess no photograph of this prince of eccentrics. He objected to being taken in any position save from the rear—a rather inadequate method of portraiture ; the bust of him, fashioned in old age, strikes me as chill and unsympathetic, but

the frontispiece to the third volume of the Essays
may give some idea of his whimsical and kindly
nature. Not that he could not fight. He fought
his zoological contemporaries and enjoyed many a
lusty bout with Audubon and " Master Swainson "
and Macgillivray; he fought the Treasury, he
fought his neighbours. He fought above all things
that Protestantism which had despoiled his grand-
fathers of their worldly goods in the days of " Saint
Harry the Eighth, our Royal Goat." While praying
for unbelievers—

> " I pray for those who now have got
> A creed infected with the rot,
> And wickedly have set at nought
> That which our ancestors had taught. . . .
>
> Again, for those I often pray,
> Who tread in Luther's crooked way;
> Or Calvin trust, or seek salvation
> In Mrs. Southcote's proclamation—"

he invented, simultaneously, a truly Watertonian
device of giving vent to his bellicose feelings by
projecting all Lutheran misdeeds, past, present, and
to come, into the *corpus vile* of an insignificant
quadruped—to wit, the brown or " Hanoverian " rat.
This miserable rodent, because it was presumably
introduced by " Dutch William," became for him
the embodiment of non-Catholic propensities and
was persecuted with the ardour of a Torquemada.
For the rest, he was a man of peace; an autoch-
thonous gentleman of the north country—the finest

flower of generations of crusted, fox-hunting Tories.
A man of merits, too; a pioneer of taxidermy, and
a tireless observer. But, chiefest of all, a peram-
bulating repository of fads and perversities.

Those Essays of his are a kind of intellectual
backwater. They seem to have been written on
another planet. And yet, somehow or other, they
are intensely human; so unsystematic; so very
English in their glorious irrelevancies. He ambles
through a hundred pages of a " History of the
Monkey Family "—stranger history was never
written; discourses amiably of this and that; argues
whether monkeys throw missiles or not; relates his
friendship with a caged lady-chimpanzee and how,
on departing, he implanted a soft kiss on her
maidenly cheek; and concludes with the startling
proposition that monkeys are arboreal animals.
He can be as pompously platitudinous as you like:
" Inhabitants of Scarbro—I love to pass my
leisure hours amongst you. May you ever prosper.
But, observe! although old Ocean rolls his favours
on you, your Mother Earth has not been quite so
bountiful: for you cannot boast a river. . . ."
" Who can look without rapture on the beautiful
proportions of the horse? His mane hanging down
a well-formed neck seems a counterbalance to his
long, flowing tail as he moves along; and we are all
of us aware of what amazing advantage this last-
mentioned appendage is to this noble beast, when a
host of flies are ready to devour him. . . ."

But though all of these Essays are saturated with the author's rich idiosyncrasies, the most poignant revelation of his incongruous nature is that autobiography which runs alongside. There is a smack of the Grand Tour lingering in this record of a leisurely progress through the regions of continental Europe; a smack, too, of a decidedly queer outlook upon things in general:

" At Rimini, now celebrated for its miraculous picture of the blessed Virgin, we could see the larger and smaller species of bats, on wing, as the night set in. Here, again, large turkeys and common fowls were most numerous. . . . Fleas were vigorously skipping about, but we neither saw nor felt a bug."

One can imagine the impression created by such a man at a civilised foreign town like Aix-la-Chapelle. He never drank wine or beer; he never slept in bed; he never wore a hat or boots; he spoke and dressed oddly; he got up every morning at 3.30 and spent his time dissecting crayfish or anything else that came handy. What did the hotel servants and visitors think of him?

I know perfectly well what they thought.

Der verrückte Engländer!

He is, he must be, a specimen of that "mad Englishman" whose tradition still lingers here and there. Only think what he did in Rome. To begin with, the road happening to be in bad repair, he arrived at the Eternal City with his feet in such a condition that he was laid up for two months on a sofa (he was always doing foolish things with his bare feet, and always suffering for them). Hardly is he well again before he climbs up the angel that surmounts the castle of Sant' Angelo and takes his stand, on one foot, on its head—a position that would have made any self-respecting chamois sea-sick. All Rome rings with the exploit: even the Pope becomes interested in the mad son of Albion. Now Waterton, a devout Catholic, would dearly have liked an audience of His Holiness, and the thing might have been managed if—if the Squire could have been induced to put on some English (Protestant) uniform for the occasion. But no. The Hanoverian rat![1]

To console himself, he watches the pig-killing operations at the slaughter-house, compiles a careful catalogue of the birds that are exposed for sale in the market, haggles with small boys about rock thrushes' eggs, and spends fabulous sums in the purchase of sham masterpieces of art. At last all is ready for departure: eighty birds have been preserved, as well as a porcupine, a badger, some shellfish and a dozen land tortoises.

He departs; but not alone. With him go, in a roomy cage, a dozen living owls. And thereby

[1] As to donning the ceremonious black evening clothes, it was utterly out of the question, since he detested that colour and could not bring himself to wear it. He rested his head at night, by the way, on a hollowed block of wood, his cheek reposing on the outward soles of his shoes "which were furnished with a profusion of strong nails." This proves (among other things) that he did not always go barefoot.

hangs a tale. For these owls, squeezed through the Genoa customs-house by hook or by crook, suffer a serious mishap on reaching Aix-la-Chapelle. The fact is, their plumage had become soiled from the long journey, even as Waterton himself was somewhat inconvenienced by its effects; somewhat dirty, to put it frankly. Warm water is plainly desirable, and it stands to reason that what is good for the Squire is also good for the owls. Waterton orders a hot bath for himself, and another one for the owls. They get it. " Five of them," he records, " died of cold the same night."

I would give my ears to see the procession winding up the drive of Walton Hall after one of these Continental raids and pilgrimages. Even on ordinary occasions the domain must have been a sight for the gods. For if the Squire as a human being was full of irresponsible fancies, here the whole region oozed eccentricity. Freaks stared you in the face. The park contained an agglomeration of weird contrivances for catching this and killing that; the mansion, beginning at the very door-knocker, was a nightmare of monstrosities and playfully-ghoulish surprises. Your head swam; you were bewildered, dazed by freaks.

And the arch-freak was the owner himself.

On his fourth trip to South America (1824) he traversed a portion of the United States—drawn thither, largely, by the descriptions he had read in Wilson's *Ornithology*. He was hugely pleased with the *gentle and civil people*, and more particularly by the ladies, to whose attractions he reverts again and again: " Nothing can surpass the appearance of the American ladies when they take their morning walk, from twelve to three, in Broadway. The stranger will at once see that they have rejected the extravagant superfluities which appear in the London and Parisian fashions,"— here follows a characteristic disquisition on women's hats—" They seem to have an abhorrence (and a very just one) of wearing caps. . . . How would Canova's Venus look in a mob cap? " He talks of the " immense number of highly polished females who go in the stages to visit the different places of amusement," adding that " words can hardly do justice to their unaffected ease and elegance."

At New York, " all charges included, you do not pay more than two dollars a day. Little enough, when you consider the capital accommodation, and the abundance of food." Buffalo, too, possesses a *fine and commodious inn*. Here, in stepping out of the stage coach, the Squire had the misfortune to sprain his foot, an accident which he recorded, in one of those polite verse-effusions to which he was subject, in some lines beginning:

> " He sprained his foot and hurt his toe,
> On the rough road near Buffalo,
> It quite distresses him to stagger a-
> Long the sharp rocks of famed Niagara."

Now, to spray an inflamed joint with cold water is clearly the correct treatment. But everything in America being on a grand scale, the traveller's ideas become enlarged as he journeys through the country, and he soon discovers that the watering-can or village pump, which might have ministered to an injured limb in England, are hopelessly out of place; bigger forces must be requisitioned; nothing in fact will serve the occasion save to hobble painfully down and suspend the swollen ankle under the cataract of Niagara. This is Waterton all over. After that he goes to Canada, and " in all the way from Buffalo to Quebec I only met with one bug; and I cannot even swear that it belonged to the United States." It was a half-grown, ill-conditioned beast, and instead of being treated after the manner of its kind it was " quietly chucked among some baggage that was close by, and recommended to get ashore by the first opportunity." Who but Waterton would have recorded such an incident? While thinking himself quite a natural person, he was temperamentally incapable of behaving like anybody else.

Gilbert White, no doubt, was his intellectual ancestor. But White had an industry and full-blooded zeal which the other lacked; he was discriminating, purposeful, constructive; altogether, a luminous creature and of relatively modern texture. Waterton is more readable than naturalists like Jesse on account of his all-pervading personal note; but, taken all round, he still remains chiefly conspicuous for his negative qualities, for his splendid limitations. He had no spacious view of life—no view at all, save through a certain narrow telescope that restricted the field of vision, intensifying one tract at the expense of all the others. What the world presented to his eyes was an assemblage of disconnected facts which it was his business not to co-ordinate or explain, but only to record. Tobacco-smoking is a beastly habit; to wear an amulet against sudden death is an excellent idea; man does not kill his fellows, because there is a law written in his heart forbidding him to do so —and the widgeon eats grass. Such is " Dame Nature's " *pre-ordained decree*. She knows what is good for everything and everybody; and if she sometimes makes a mistake or exceeds her *mandate* —why, there is always God overhead, to put things to rights again.

So he lived, this mellow country gentleman; at once a warning and an exemplar, like the rest of us. He had a birdlike habit of pecking at all sorts of mental pabulum, and allowing it to pass out of his system half-digested. His worldly experiences never resolved themselves into a truthful whole, for Stonyhurst, if it fortified his moral sense, had warped and atrophied his mind, rendering him permanently unsynthetic—fragmentary in every point save one: his crankiness. In that he was superb. If a man took thought for a lifetime he could never figure forth a more harmonious and lovable freak. As grotesque as that old fowl of Mauritius, he is nowadays, alas! almost as rare. For phœnixes are all very well, but we do need an occasional dodo to diversify the landscape.

Darwin may quote from the original and accurate observations of the Yorkshire squire, but what does Waterton care for the portentous movement of his later life—what, indeed, does he know of any of those landmarks like Homer or Dante or Goethe? He had been fed on orthodox pap, on Virgil, Dryden, and other *safe* writers; and it is a suggestive commentary on our social state that this mighty personage, the twenty-seventh Lord of Walton, should be disqualified by his creed from attaining that elementary knowledge of the world which was at the disposal of the poorest peasant-boy on his estate. To chronicle the matrimonial irregularities of the barnacle gander; to feed your unsuspecting guests on a dish of carrion crows and chuckle inwardly at their mistaking them for pigeons; to jump at the age of seventy-nine over a formidable wire fence; to rush with furious growls from under the hall table at your visitors' legs, pretending (at the age of eighty) to be house-dog—these were his aims and diversions.

It was one of his jocular habits to give names to the more prominent animals and trees in his park.

N

Among the birds there was a malformed wild duck, deprived of the web between its toes, which Waterton had received as a gift " in an ecstasy of delight " —seeing that everything in the nature of a " sport " struck a chord of elective affinity, an echo in his own eccentric nature, and warmed the cockles of his heart. This bird was forthwith christened " Doctor Hobson."

Its human original, a physician of Leeds, was himself something of an ornithologist who became acquainted with Waterton during the latter part of his life, and took charge of his health—as best he could. In after years he wrote an account of the " Home, Habits and Handicraft " of his friend which is truly refreshing—a kind of showerbath—in these oppressive days of psycho-analysis and sex-problems. Doctor Hobson revered the Squire and all his little failings; he assimilated his curiously tangled and wayward style of writing; he has entered into the very bones of his hero. And not all of us, be it noted, are heroes to our medical advisers. This biography is a fine monument of friendship; even as the friendship itself says much for the characters of both of them, since Waterton's peculiarities might well have repelled other men of science. I suspect that the unswerving uprightness of the Squire won the doctor's affection; that little incident at Leeds, too, when Waterton with incredible nerve and steadiness of hand removed twenty-eight rattlesnakes from one box into

another, may well have impressed a medicine-man,
conscious of the ever-present risk of death.

Be that as it may, our naturalist has found
a Boswell after his own heart; the enthusiastic
reporter of all his anfractuosities and gentlemanly
pranks; one who has given to the more intimate
" Squire " that congenial and efficient interpretation
which Sydney Smith gave to the public Waterton of
the *Wanderings*. The Table of Contents alone
of this remarkable book is a joy for ever. It contains
items like this: An Ox-Eye Titmouse builds her
Nest in the Trunk of a Tree prepared for Owls,
but declines occupying it in future years because a
Squirrel had used it. Or this: Discriminating
Courage of the Squire with an Ourang-Outang from
Borneo, in the Zoological Gardens—followed by:
The Ape Searching the Squire's head reminds
him of a Cambridge anecdote. Or take these
stimulating entries: An Allusion to a stench from
a dead herring near the Grotto induces the Squire
to relate an incident regarding dead letters. . . .
Mr. Waterton faces a snowstorm without his Hat,
and throws his Slippers over his head when
approaching his eightieth year. . . . Mr. Waterton
distressed because his Bahia toad was called an
" Ugly Brute! "

The volume is full of stupendous things of this
kind; it reproduces also some of the Squire's letters,
which illustrate the childlike texture of his mind:

" I don't care who holds the helm of our crazy

vessel, so long as ' Mummery John ' does not get hold of it. You did not arrive according to promise. We hope to be more fortunate on Palm Sunday after you have requested your spiritual adviser to keep a blessed palm for you, when he delivers the sprigs to the assembled multitude from his altar. Stop, I ought to say table. Many thanks for your communication. I hope that you will pursue the investigation. It is somewhat singular that I have never yet found the large bone in the wings of water-fowl full of marrow. . . ." [1]

There is another entry to this effect : The Squire remonstrated with by the Author against too frequently "tapping the Claret." This excessive "tapping the Claret "—bleeding himself—was one of the few traits of which the physician-biographer disapproved. Whatever happened to Waterton— whether he ate too much, or tumbled off a mule, or had an accident with his gun, or caught a chill— out with the lancet! Even in his eightieth year he did not hesitate to bleed himself to the tune of twenty to twenty-four ounces at a time; he must have lost a barrelful of the precious liquid in the course of his long life. His horses were bled with the same recklessness—what was good for the Squire being obviously good for them. In the jungle he tried to induce the vampire-bat to bleed him; many a night, he says, " have I slept with my foot out of

[1] Some charming letters are preserved in Dr. Norman Moore's edition of the *Essays*.

the hammock to tempt this winged surgeon "—in
vain! He was dry as a stick, and the sagacious
vespertilian sought its dinner elsewhere.

And of course his ultra-Catholic tendencies were
not quite to the taste of Hobson who, however,
deals gently with such infirmities, merely suggesting that he " had an inordinate amount of credulity
in his composition." Indeed he had. He was a
Catholic *comme il faut*. Reared in the unrelenting
machinery of Stonyhurst, he was cut into its cleanest
pattern, and preserved throughout life its edges
intact, its surface untarnished. No imposture was
too fantastic for him to swallow. He travelled
expressly to the Tyrol to see an ecstatic female in
a convent, and convinced himself of her divine state
by feeling the stigma on one of her hands. Nothing
in his whole life, he says, struck him so forcibly as
the liquefaction, at Naples, of the mixture which he
devoutly held to be the blood of Saint Januarius.
He speaks with reverent awe of Benedict Labre—
that half-witted vagabond, who never washed or
took off his clothes, and was covered from head to
foot with vermin which he refused to exterminate.
And although a belief in the miraculous transporta-
tion of the House of the Blessed Virgin is optional
to his co-religionists, yet he writes that there are
authentic proofs of the aerial voyage of this mansion
over lands and seas and that, for his part, he believes
in the miracle.

Doctor Hobson's chief concern was to mitigate

the severity of those periodical abstinences from food which the Squire's stern Catholicism imposed upon him. As for the House of Loreto and the like—he had too much tolerance to disquiet himself about such discrepancies. Birds are birds and men are men; all of them liable to variations and each of these variations ordained for dark providential reasons. A sparrow hops and a wagtail runs: shall all human beings think and behave alike? And if inclined, at times, to regret his friend's " ardent attachment to the priests," he amply compensated himself by praising his sincere love of nature, his rectitude and guileless purity of heart and—last, not least—those flexible lower extremities which enabled him, as a hoary patriarch, to scratch the back part of his head with the big toe of his right foot or to clamber aloft, with the agility of an adolescent gorilla, into the breezy summit of an oak.

And here we may leave this *par nobile fratrum:* Æsculapius on earth, fondly admiring but— prudent; his ever-youthful octogenarian comrade perched in the verdurous foliage overhead, reading Ovid's *Metamorphoses* and glancing occasionally through a spy-glass to see whether the Rumpless Fowl, that preposterous and unmatronly bird, has at last thought fit to hatch her own offspring in accordance with Dame Nature's pre-ordained decree.

QUEER!

Queer!

THEY sat there in the sunshine, discussing many things that had happened to themselves during the long three years' interval since their last meeting, and occasionally glancing up to admire some pretty face or to greet an acquaintance in the coloured throng that moved ceaselessly to and fro before their eyes.

Presently there was a lull, a sudden break, in the conversation. It lasted some little time. Then one of the two, speaking rather slowly, made a commonplace remark. He observed:

"It has only this instant struck me how odd it was that we should have run up against each other in this fashion." He said not another word. He seemed to be thinking hard.

"Hyde Park," replied his friend, "on a fine morning in May, is quite a likely place for two people to meet, isn't it? Why odd? I don't see anything odd about it."

"I do. More than odd, because I understood you were still in East Africa and because—"

"I told you I came back a month ago."

"And because I happened to be thinking about

201

you, I don't know why, at the very moment when you sprang out of the earth in front of me. There you were! Now why were you there? Just tell me what you were doing there? Damn it all," he suddenly broke in, "you aren't another ghost, by any chance? You aren't still in Dar-es-Salam, are you? Let's have a good look at you."

"Try one of these," said the other. "They're uncommonly mild. That ought to convince you. Ghosts don't carry Turkish cigarettes about, do they?"

"I'm not sure about that; not at all sure," replied the first speaker, as though weighing the pros and cons of such a possibility with judicial deliberation. Then he went on, more gravely than before: "It would take more than a cigarette to convince me one way or the other. You don't believe in ghosts?"

"Ghosts? My dear fellow, since when are you interested in ghosts? I don't know anything about them. I'm supposed to be dreadfully matter-of-fact. I never yet saw one."

"Nor did I; not of the intangible kind; the kind that struts about at night frightening people out of their wits. I can't say I ever saw a ghost of that variety. But I have seen something worse than that within a few hundred yards of where we are now sitting, and less than a year ago. That is why I'm not altogether certain even now whether—well, whether you aren't out of England after all. Don't suppose I'm joking. I may as well tell you that I've had a pretty bad jar since last we met. Something infinitely worse," he added in a low voice.

" Infinitely worse," echoed his friend incredulously. " Look here, oughtn't you perhaps to see a doctor? "

" This one, you see, came in daylight. My thoughts seemed to conjure it up. There it was! It sprang out of the earth and accosted me, just as you did ten minutes ago. And that's what made me wonder. . . . Let's have another look at you. . . . No," he went on, in a calmer tone, " I don't fancy such things are allowed to happen to a man more than once in his lifetime. I hope not. I don't suppose you are anywhere but in the Park at present. Yet the ghost I saw was as tangible as you are. I touched it; I talked to it. I dined with it! Believe me or not, I smoked some of its cigars—"

" My dear fellow—"

" Two of them. And I can't say that it actually frightened me. Not at the time, anyhow. But I got a good scare later on; a thundering scare. You have heard me speak of O'Beirne? "

" Your agricultural expert? " queried his friend.

" Expert? Well, not exactly an expert. An enthusiast, you might call him; a burly, kind-hearted faddist; a maniac with streaks of commonsense here and there. And so good-natured! He never can do enough for you. I know it well, because I often stayed with him in County ——. It's all bog, you know, that place of his; nothing but bog; a desolation of black bog. That is precisely what gave him his chance as an agriculturist. He meant to show those people what you could do in the way of getting your money's worth out of a bog; model farmhouses and that kind of thing. He built a decent bridge or two and laid down roads and started drainage-works and imported incubators and outlandish seeds and sanitary pig-sties and God knows what. I suspect it made him rather unpopular over there; the Irish don't take kindly to these fantastic Anglo-Saxon notions; besides, trust me, they know their bog! But nothing could stop him. At last he caught the beetroot craze. He was going to produce sugar on a respectable scale; and he crossed over to Germany or Belgium to get up the subject, and came back all glowing with optimism. I told him before he left that you could hardly expect beets to grow in a bog that might be a hundred or a thousand feet deep. He said he had thought it all over years and years ago and that nothing I could put forward would alter his plans; that the Irish only needed a little encouragement on the part of well-to-do people like himself; that his beets might possibly suffer at first, but could not help acclimatising themselves in the long run. They might develop into a slightly different race, a bog-loving race: why not? There was no reason to anticipate that the sugary qualities of the root would suffer in consequence of the change of environment; on the contrary, they might even be improved by the peculiar soil; the Irish potato, for instance, an alien to the country—wasn't it now the finest in the world?"

"Sheer madness," commented his friend.

"Of course it was. Sheer madness; a generous form of madness; any sensible Irishman could have told him— Well, that was the last time I saw O'Beirne. But I often thought of him. I was thinking of him more particularly one evening last August as I walked along Piccadilly on my way to dinner at the Club. Last August; the twenty-first. Now what made me stay on so late in town? Was it just laziness? Very likely. Or perhaps I may have been a bit run down as well; I believe I was. Anyhow, there I happened to be, and you know how insufferable London is at that season, with clusters of loathsome creatures lying about the parks, and a sickly haze hanging over everything, as if streets and houses and even the sky itself needed a thorough spring-cleaning. What a hateful place! You perspire all day and sink into the half-melted asphalt as you walk along, and fill your lungs with bad air and toss about your bed at night and wake up with a headache every morning—that peculiar London headache; you know it? I thought: why not clear out of this noisome, rowdy hole? And I began to wonder how O'Beirne was getting on with

his beetroots and to wish I were with him in County
——, as I was the August before.

" Now I know you don't like Ireland. A good
many people don't seem to like Ireland. No doubt
one can say bad things about it, any amount of them,
but this you must admit : there is a unique quality
in the scenery of those boggy parts, especially in
autumn. It's a sort of yearning charm. If you
want something different from this London life,
something completely different, don't go to Switzer-
land or Africa or China; go to O'Beirne's place.
You can discover sensations there that I defy you
to discover anywhere else. Something infinitely
poor and primeval, I mean, with those sluggish
waters and lowering skies all drowned in a mournful,
mysterious twilight. Something unchanging too,
quite unlike this country; you gain a conviction of
immemorial sameness—not an inch of those weary
boreal outlines has altered since the day of creation
or ever will alter; unchanging and at the same time
so simple, so featureless, so monotonous, that God
must obviously have forgotten to insert the main
ingredients of the landscape : gone off in a doze,
I should say, before putting in His usual final
touches. Hence its dissimilarity to other countries.
At least, that is my impression of the place; an
impression of fabulous remoteness from the ordinary
resorts of men. I feel as if I had been left stranded
in some drowsy, neglected nook at the outer rim of
the world, on the borderland of emptiness; some

faint and pale region made for Shadows and not human beings to inhabit. And then, the strangely wonderful scent of peat-burning which haunts you like a melody! And those utter silences—how different from all the senseless noise and bustle and stench of London!

"Well, I was thinking of this dreamland of O'Beirne's as I walked along Piccadilly that evening; thinking so longingly that I got into a kind of mazy dream myself, a dream that made me positively homesick for him and his bogs and beet-roots; so homesick that, for once in the way, I had a sudden and brilliant inspiration. I thought:

"I've half a mind—By Jove! what's to prevent me from running over to Kingston to-morrow? He is sure to be delighted to see me; he always is."

"And you went?" enquired his friend.

"I would have gone. I didn't have to go because, at that very moment, I ran up against O'Beirne himself; in fact, we ran into each other."

"What a surprise, eh?"

"'This is a rare piece of luck,' he began at once. 'Delighted to see you again! It's ages since we met, and I was just wondering what had happened to you. I only came over two days ago to look at a mare of Carborough's, but she is not up to my weight. What do you say to dining somewhere? And tell me your news as we go along. Or are you engaged?'

" I looked at him. He was a little older, of course, but otherwise unchanged except that his hair had turned nearly grey and that, contrary to his usual habit, he was wearing a terribly flashy suit with a flamboyant neck-tie. It struck me as far too vulgar for a man of his style. I said:

" ' I was just on the way to a solitary dinner at my Club. Come along with me. You used to like the port, I remember, and they've generally got a decent joint—'

" ' An English club? Thanks. I'd rather not, if you don't mind. I think I know a better place.'

" ' Have it your way.'

" We entered a restaurant at the back of Regent Street, the ' Parisian '; not cheap and nasty but— well, full of foreigners, which amounts to practically the same thing for me. The only Englishman I saw there was Frankie Sumner, the Academician, sitting gloomily at a table by himself. You know Frankie? Solemn old fool, isn't he? That is his notion, you know, of being an authentic cosmopolitan, a Bohemian of the first water; to eat his chop, all alone, in a frowsy foreign restaurant. I exchanged a few words with him and we passed on.

" ' You're wearing a tasty suit this evening,' I began, as soon as we had taken our seats. I couldn't get over that outfit, you observe. It was too loud for anything.

" ' Damn my clothes,' he said. ' I'll tell you

something that will interest you much more. I've
married Lucy.'

" ' Your housekeeper? Congratulations! But
isn't she—' a little old and not quite your class, I
was going to add. Luckily I pulled up short. He
may have guessed my thoughts all the same.

" ' A person of my age marries whom he pleases.
And if he waited for a week of Sundays he couldn't
do better than select such a perfect specimen of his
race. I've lost all interest in other women. Waiter!
Just bring me a cutlet that's fit for man's
consumption, and be sharp about it.'

" It had already struck me as we walked along
that we did not seem to be hitting it off quite as well
as usual. He was different, somehow, from the
jovial and smiling O'Beirne I used to know. What
can have come over him, I wondered?

" ' Lost your interest in women? ' I began again.
' Bad luck! But you have lost something else as
well, something even more precious, something you
ought to have kept at all costs: your lovely Irish
brogue. What wouldn't I give to have it! '

" ' No, I haven't lost that. I have only put it in
cold storage. I reserve my brogue for Ireland
nowadays. Waiter! Did you hear what I said? '

" The waiter was at the other end of the room
just then, and well out of ear-shot.

" I made another attempt.

" ' How are the beetroots doing? '

" ' Beetroots? Ah, yes; I remember. They

were doing splendidly. I thought they would! You never saw such a crop. But I have had them pulled up, every jack one of them. And I am now thinking of burning the whole house down as well. It's our only hope. Waiter!'

" ' Yessir? '

" ' Go to Hell.'

" ' My dear boy,' I said, ' you've been drinking.'

" ' Half a pint of bad Médoc for luncheon and nothing since then, if you call that drinking. I've not been drinking. I've been thinking. Now do have some more of this Camembert.' And he broke off again. Distinctly bizarre he was, that evening; not to say snappy.

" ' Thanks. I will.' I said nothing else because I really didn't know how to take him. He said nothing either.

" There we sat.

" ' Thinking about what? ' I enquired at last. He burst out:

" ' Not a day of decent government since they set foot in the place! It's our only hope. Blow everything to pieces. Get the country into such a filthy mess that the bullying brutes don't want it any more—'

" Don't imagine I am going to repeat all the incoherent swashbuckling nonsense he poured out later, over the coffee; I could never remember it if I tried. Only note this: it was not the talk of a blustering Irish patriot. It was the talk of a down-

right lunatic. And he got worse and worse and
more and more excited and dictatorial; almost
offensive, I should call it. I wished I had never
sat down to dine with him. People began staring
at us till I felt ashamed of being seen in his company.
He banged the table and roared at the waiters and
made such an exhibition of himself that old Frankie,
a few days afterwards, asked me who my eccentric
friend had been and whether I got home quite safe
that night. And while he was raving along like
this I kept on asking myself what on earth could
be the matter with him. He had changed amazingly
in the interval since our last meeting. Or was
anything the matter with me? Could I be really
awake? Because all the time—yes, all the time—
I was aware of a singular feeling, a dreamy sense of
oppression and dislocation; a sense of unreality. I
seemed to be addressing not himself but some nightmarish distortion of his old, lovable personality.
And then his eyes—they gradually developed a
ravenous and unsteady look; something infernally
unpleasant. What was it? Hanged if I knew!
Whatever it was, you may be sure our dinner was a
failure, a dismal failure; as rotten a dinner as I can
remember. At the end of it he left his chair rather
abruptly and cleared out; said he had an appointment with a man about some patent fuses. Of
course he never asked me to stay in County ——;
not he! And thank God for that. I should
certainly have made an excuse, for I had meanwhile

registered a vow to drop his acquaintance and give him a wide berth in future. One really can't be seen about with a bounder like that, even in the bogs of ——; can one? "

And here the speaker paused, as if undecided how to continue his narrative.

His friend said:

" That was certainly a strange meeting. And you never saw him again? "

" Him? Whom? "

" Why, O'Beirne, of course."

" O'Beirne? I never saw him at all. What I met in Piccadilly last August was something else."

" You don't mean to say—"

" I saw my friend, the real O'Beirne, about five weeks later. He is just the same as he always was, not grey-haired and not married to this day; in fact as different as can be from the meaningless and unlovely caricature of himself that I had dined with. Needless to add, he was simply dumbfounded when I told him the story. What do you say to that? "

" Queer. Queer. Decidedly queer."

" Yes. And at the time of our presumable meeting he was in charge of some Red Cross work in the Dolomites. Altogether, the most odious and ghastly experience I've ever had; I don't suppose I shall get over it as long as I live. Can you explain it? "

The other thought a while and then said:

" I cannot explain it at all. There must be some hanky-panky somewhere. If it weren't for the fact that Sumner was an eye-witness—"

" Exactly! You'd say I had been suffering from some kind of hallucination, wouldn't you? But Frankie was there, and you know what a precise old Bohemian he is; you can see it in his pictures. Ask him about the incident any day you like! He remembers it perfectly. He was chaffing me only last week again about my obstreperous foreign friend, and whether I really got home that night without having my head bashed in. Something so insane and impertinent about the whole business. . . . What did the devilish affair come for? What did it want with me? What was it doing in Piccadilly, to begin with? Made me look like a regular fool, damn it, before all those people. Can you make anything out of it, eh? "

" Nothing. I've already told you that; and when I can't explain a thing, I leave it alone. Look here, why not go for a stroll? "

" Nothing? Is that all you have to say? Nothing? This is very unsatisfactory. I thought you might be able to help me somehow, or to suggest a solution. Can't you? You know it's been a beastly jar to me."

" I can well believe it, and perhaps you had better see a doctor after all. That sort of thing would be enough to make anyone feel uncomfortable, though I doubt whether I should still be taking it as seriously as you do. Now please don't think me unsympathetic because I happen to be rather matter-of-fact and incurious, not to say sceptical. All these so-called mysteries, every one of them, are cleared up scientifically sooner or later, aren't they? Therefore, if you could just bring yourself to wait another two or three hundred years, or even less—"

" Very unsatisfactory."

" So it is; so it is. I only wish I could help you! Now let's take a stroll."

" Because, you understand, if this were an isolated case, if you could swear to me that such a thing can never occur again, I should be happy as a king. Will you swear it? Of course you won't. Then how do I know that there are not more such miserable horrors fluttering around, dozens, hundreds of them, masquerading in flesh and blood and playing their foul tricks on one or the other of us; how am I to be certain—dead certain, I mean —that you, for example—"

" Look here, my dear fellow. You may take me for a ghost if it suits your convenience, though I don't consider it very polite of you. Anyhow, ghost or no ghost, I'm tired of sitting down. I want to stretch my legs. I must stretch my legs. Suppose we toddle up to the Serpentine? "

" As you please. But this is very, very unsatisfactory. If it hadn't been for old Frankie . . . Oh, and I asked O'Beirne about those beetroots. He told me they were not doing quite as well as he hoped; all rather ailing and flabby; in fact, not yet properly acclimatised. A thin crop, he called it. Of course it was merely a question of time. Meanwhile the dear old boy is as keen as ever, and says he thinks of trying some experiments with maize or hemp, or cotton."

" Why not bananas? "

ANACREONTIC

Anacreontic

(Cowley-Fashion)

Nimble wagtail, wherefore run
In the fiery noonday sun?
Sprightly fowl, in livery gray,
Why not shun the scorching ray,
Why not rest a while content
Till Apollo's rage relent?
I, secure in rosy bowers,
Dream away the flaming hours—
Dream away in slumberous ease
Fears that harass, doubts that tease;
Dream, and with prophetic eye
Jove's exalted aims espy.
His arrangement wisely bends
All his works to various ends:
Sparrows hop and lizards creep,
Wagtails run and sages sleep.
Jove for things of every kind
Happiness contrives to find,
Into every element
Some inhabitant he's sent.
In the *earth's* recesses bleak

Sightless moles their substance seek,
In the *air* the gnats meander,
In the *fire* the salamander
Broods upon the crimson flame.
Wagtail, you your tastes proclaim
By the *water* cool and clear
Of the silver-margined mere.
Sober one! I envy not
Such an unconvivial lot.
Watery fashions I disdain.
Give me wine! All else is vain.
Some with hoarded gold are blest—
Give me wine! And take the rest.
Hark'ee, wagtail: Mend your ways;
Life is brief, Anacreon says,
Brief its joys, its ventures toilsome;
Wine befriends them—water spoils 'em.
Who's for water? Wagtail, you?
Give me wine! I'll drink for two.

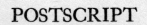

POSTSCRIPT

Postscript

A Plea for Better Manners

SOME kind person, with belated thoughtful-
ness, has just sent me a short article from
the London *Outlook* of 1st November,
wherein I find myself mentioned in connection with
those recently published *Memoirs of a Private in
the Foreign Legion* to which D. H. Lawrence has
supplied an Introduction. The writer of the article
opines that the " N. D." depicted by Lawrence must
be myself.

Is it?

Why, of course it is. There is no mistaking
that "wicked red face," those shabby clothes
coupled with the bluff, grandiose manner of what
may once have been a gentleman. I should
recognise myself at a mile's distance, especially
knowing, as I do, friend Lawrence's idiosyncrasies
in the matter of portraiture; what he contrives to
see and what he fails to see; or rather, what he
makes a point of seeing, and what he makes a point
of not seeing. For he is not congenitally blind; he
is only blind when it suits his convenience. He
sees, for instance, that after a certain dinner I ask
the waiter to weigh the remaining wine and take its

price off the bill—which makes me look a little mean (quite a gentlemanly trait, nowadays); he fails to see that in restaurants of this class wine is invariably sold by weight, and that the man who does not act as I did is held to be weak in the head. He also sees that I don't believe in opening windows on November evenings—in other words, that I am a nitrogen-maniac; he does not see that nitrogen is an antidote to sleeplessness, that a healthy man gets quite enough fresh air out of doors without cramming his house full of the stuff, and that, in fact, this whole oxygen-cult is nothing but humbug, and, in the winter months, downright lunacy.

I have no fault to find with this travesty of myself; no fault whatever; it is perfectly legitimate fooling, and my young friend might have presented me in far less engaging fashion, since I gave him permission to "put me in as you please." He might have—well, there is no knowing what he might not have done or what he may not yet do, if the impish mood is upon him. Altogether: capital reading, Lawrence's Introduction, although in places not only incorrect but woefully wrong-headed; indeed, a masterpiece of unconscious misrepresentation. I hope it will help to sell the book; I hope that I, who am entitled to half the proceeds, will in due course receive something on account. But he has not been fair to Maurice Magnus, the Private whose Memoirs are here published; and I am inclined to agree with the writer of the *Outlook* article who on the strength of some information received—both the writer and his informant are unknown to me—says that far from being a " scamp and a treacherous little devil," as described by Lawrence, Magnus was "not only a brave man, but one who was witty and amusing and most likeable." . . .

All this is awkward. One hates thrusting oneself forward in a matter of this kind; it smacks of bad form, and life is already too full of unnecessary personalities. But I am dragged into the business by name, and there seems to be no way out of it, especially as, being Maurice's literary executor, I have received letters from several people asking what I am going to do about it. You knew him well, they say. Was he really as much of a "bounder" as Lawrence makes out? Can't you tell us the truth?

I wish I could. I suffer under a double drawback. In the first place, I like to taste my friends but not to eat them; in other words, I hold the old-fashioned view that all interrogation, all social curiosity, is vulgar and therefore to be avoided; the consequence being that, in the present case, I know practically nothing about his past, having never asked anything. Next, I have been unable to obtain access to those papers which he left me at his death and which might allow me to write some kind of a sketch of his feverishly restless existence. I have seen these papers, a suit-case

P

full of them: they consist of family documents and diaries; literary material of many kinds; letters from important persons in every walk of life— musical and theatrical celebrities beginning with Paderewski, Sarah Bernhardt, Duse; American millionaires, Russian Grand Dukes, a crowned head or two (only Balkans, I fear), etc., etc. I have seen them. That is all.

Now, at the risk of being long-winded, I will try to straighten this affair out definitely. On learning of his suicide, I applied for these papers, including the Foreign Legion Memoirs, to the gentleman in Malta whom Lawrence calls Mr. Mazzaiba in whose possession they then were and presumably still are; with negative results.[1] And this in spite of a memorandum written by Magnus shortly before his death (quoted by Lawrence on p. 83) which contains words to this effect: "My literary executor Norman Douglas (address). . . . All manuscripts and books for Norman Douglas. . . . I leave my literary property to Norman Douglas to whom half of the results are to accrue— the other half my debts are to be paid with." That strikes me as plain speaking. Magnus being an American citizen, I next applied to his Consul in Malta on December 22nd, 1920. I wrote: "Regarding the literary materials of Mr. Magnus, I suppose they had better be sent here (to Mentone).

---

[1] There has been no reply to a recent application on my part.

I may be able to dispose of some of his manuscripts and would hand over the proceeds towards the settlement of his accounts." The Consul thought my suggestion "very reasonable and, under ordinary circumstances, the obvious thing to do." There were difficulties, however—difficulties I shall not enter upon here, since my only desire is to draw attention to what were Magnus' clear wishes on the subject of these papers. And that this memorandum was not a sudden afterthought on his part is proved by a letter to me, dated 4th May, 1920, in which he says : " I leave all my manuscripts and papers to you—and their proceeds." He also once gave me the following document, imploring me to keep it in some safe place :

"ROME, *Nov. 26th*, 1919.

" In case of my death all my literary material and letters, at present in N. C.'s studio in 33 Via . . . Rome, shall go to Norman Douglas without any reservation.

"MAURICE MAGNUS."

Now I can understand his poor little personal effects—his silver card case, 3 razors, 1 soft felt hat, 1 frying pan, 1 rubber bath and so forth : the whole of them inventoried officially and valued at seventy-five dollars—I can understand these things being retained in Malta with a view to paying his debts. But literary property classified as " one old leather

suit-case containing manuscripts and a carton
envelope containing photographs " hardly comes
under the same category.

Are the wishes of this dead man ever going to
be respected?

It was in Capri that I first spoke to Magnus.
I happen to know the exact date—Sunday,
22nd August, 1909. I know it because I had fixed
to leave, and did leave, that same evening for the
mountains of the Abruzzi. Somewhere about
midday a slender—yes, he was slender at that
time—and immaculately dressed young man came
up to me and, after introducing himself, began
politely, very politely, to ask for a small loan of
money. There was something childlike and for-
lorn about him. His manner was ingratiating but
not cringing; an unaffected, offhand manner,
as if he spoke about the weather or the latest
scandal.

" My dear sir," I said, " you have just come to
the right person for a loan. And who is the
damned idiot that recommended you to apply to
me ? "

Nobody, he vowed. He did not know any one
in the island. That was just it! If he only had
some friend in the place, he would probably not
have ventured. . . . But he had noticed me once
or twice in the street, and I looked so " kind " that
. . . oh, quite a small matter, only a few francs,

sufficient to enable him to run over to the mainland where he was expecting remittances which must have arrived from New York by this time. He would cash them in Naples (there was no bank on Capri in those days) in order to return here and settle up his affairs before leaving for America. Couldn't I manage it?

I said:

" I wish the devil I didn't look so kind. Anyhow, you won't get me to lend you money; I never do. It makes enemies."

" Dear, dear—"

" But I have been known to give, on occasion. Let me see—" pulling out my pocket-book grumblingly and counting up all I could spare— " would thirty-seven francs meet the case? "

It was enough, he declared. Nearly one pound ten; it was more than enough! Then, after some further protestations:

" Can you really spare it? "

" Of course I can't. But I suppose I shall have to."

" I'll never forget your kindness," he said.

In the same month of August once more, the August of 1917, we met again. He had meanwhile faded out of my memory. The same fastidiously dressed personage stopped me in the Corso in Rome, re-introduced himself and reminded me of those miserable thirty-seven francs, adding: " And now you must let me do something for you in return, if I can; you really must."

He was pretty flush just then, and I on my beam ends and altogether run down. He installed me in his apartment, cleared out of his own bedroom and gave it to me, bought me a new outfit and fed me like a prince. There I stayed, putting on flesh again; and I have only to add that from that day onwards till his death there was nothing he would not do for me; he seemed to delight in anticipating my smallest wishes. If this be what Lawrence calls an ungrateful nature, it is the kind of ingratitude I can still put up with. I observe my young friend is inclined to poke fun at Maurice's continued devotion to me in the year 1919; how he ran my errands, " indulged and spoilt me in every way " and so forth. Let him. I think it creditable to myself. Lucky the man, I say, who can inspire such a deep and lasting affection. Then he proceeds to say that I *despised* him. This is going too far; in fact, it is sheer bunkum—the novelist's touch, about which I may have something to say later on. One does not consort with people whom one despises; one does not despise people who show one a thousand kindnesses. In a book called *Alone* (p. 134) I already spoke of him as " that most charming of persons," and I never had occasion to change that opinion. Several of my letters to him were returned to me by the Malta post-office after his death; I find I wrote to him, unaware that this had already occurred, on the 6th, 8th, 14th and 15th of November, 1920. Catch me keeping up such a correspondence with a person whom I despise!

And so much for this little absurdity.

At this time he had just begun writing the Memoirs of the Foreign Legion which have led me into this disquisition. I never saw these Memoirs in their subsequent shape—in proof or even in type-script: they were then growing up slowly in manu-script, and the title he had chosen was *Dregs*, a most appropriate one which recurs in the text itself and which has been changed for reasons I cannot fathom. He used to work very hard both then and at subsequent periods of his life. It was his peculiar and insane habit to get up every morn-ing at about 4.30; he then had a bath and a shave, made his own tea and dressed himself in that costume like " a little pontiff " which Lawrence has so admirably described (I commend this short para-graph to those simpletons who say that friend Lawrence cannot write; it is a perfect etching—not a stroke too much or too little; there he is, " M. M." in matutinal garb, once and for ever). That done, he sat down at his writing-table and got through an ordinary man's daily task while most of us were still in our beds. His zest for work was terrific, non-European; it proved him to be what he was, an American; moreover, he gave you the impression of really liking it—a state of affairs which has always been unintelligible to me, who never did a stroke save under the lash of what I considered to be necessity.

At eleven or thereabouts he rose from the table which was now strewn with fresh manuscripts and letters to correspondents in every corner of the world, twenty or thirty of them done every morning. By this time he was rather tired and played out, rather "yellowish under the eyes" as Lawrence picturesquely puts it, and ready—no wonder!—for a pick-me-up in the shape of a drop of whisky. He fancied, I regret to say, a potent American brand whose name has escaped me. Being partial, myself, to the Scotch or Irish varieties, I used to taunt him with this perverse form of patriotism in the hope of bringing him round to my view and getting whisky more to my own taste; he was adamant; nothing would induce him to abate his national fervour in this respect, and therefore, as I did not want him to be everlastingly buying special bottles for me, I finally grew reconciled to the transatlantic stuff and learned to like it almost as well as he did. The sacrifices one makes for one's friends!

Sometimes, again, he interrupted his work in order to attend early Mass, since he felt utterly wretched without such periodical doses of anthropomorphism. Then he would return home, beaming all over, and say:

"I prayed ten minutes for your happiness just now."

" Very thoughtful of you, my dear boy. Though I can't say I feel any the better for it."

" You will, you will! "

" Possibly. But I always prefer to take these things in ready cash. Then you know where you are."

" You can't imagine how it hurts me, when you talk like that."

I could imagine it perfectly well. But it did him good to be reminded that not everybody was a R.C. convert; that not everybody could endure reading the Lives of the Saints and the sickly Thomas à Kempis of whom he was so fond. Often I recommended Nietzsche as a counter-irritant. That gospel would have worked wonders on his assimilative mind. He would not touch the book; perhaps it is on the Index, where I think it ought to be.

Now Lawrence, in the paragraph I have mentioned and in others, speaks of his cut-glass bottles and silver-studded suit-cases and pomades and powders and all the rest of it. This is quite correct. He was finicky and fussy and fastidious to a degree, especially about his wearing apparel; he never used any save the finest cambric handkerchiefs, and once presented me with a dozen of them, urging me not to send them to a laundry but to wash them myself, as he did. He made a fine art, almost a religion, of the folding-up and general conversation of clothes, with the consequence that during the first days I passed in his place I had prodigious fun with him. He used to bring breakfast to my bedside at a reasonable hour—say, 7.30—on a wonderful little tray, and then look round despondingly and remark :

" Rather a mess in here. I'd like to tidy the room a bit, if you don't mind, before the man comes in. Where are all your clothes? "

" They must be somewhere."

" Good gracious! Here's your shirt on the window-sill. And your trousers hanging to the top of the wardrobe. Don't you know that trousers ought to be folded up every evening? Why have you turned them inside out? "

" I suppose they came off easier that way."

" Where are your socks? "

" You might look under the bed."

" They're not there. Just try to think what you did with them. Do try."

" I know. I left them on the hall table."

" What on earth made you put them there? "

" Can't think. Perhaps I began undressing outside."

" Dear, dear. This is awful. Were you never taught to arrange your clothes before going to bed? "

" I wasn't brought up so fussily."

" And there's only one boot. Where's the other one? "

" I haven't the faintest idea. Please don't

bother about the damned thing.   You're putting me
off my breakfast."

"I mean to find that boot."

Then he would disappear for a while, and come
back in despair.

"Half my morning wasted! And your boot is
nowhere to be found."

"I remember now. In the medicine-chest . . ."

I imagine that his refinements in the matter of
toilette, and also of cookery, were due to the fact
that he was an only son, brought up by an adoring
mother and almost continually in her company to
the day of her death (she died of cancer)—that is, up
to his own *thirty-sixth* year. I wish I could relate
something about this mother who in his eyes was a
kind of sacred creature—his "great stunt," Lawrence
calls her—but a regrettable incuriosity of mine has
prevented me from learning anything of importance
save that she was an illegitimate daughter of old
William of Prussia (hence the inscription on her
tombstone in Rome: *Filia regis*).   It is true that
he began to talk about her once or twice, but his
voice at once took on such tremulously tender
accents that I lost no time in changing the conversation.   I gathered, however, that there was a bond
of more than common affection between the two,
that they were everything to each other, and that her
death was the tragedy of his life.   He told me she
had never been able to deny him anything.   It may
well be true; and herein I detect the seeds of that

habit of reckless expenditure which proved to be his undoing. Certainly her death must have given him a twist that never passed off; a twist reflected in his very face which, in unguarded moments, took on as sad an expression as I have seen on any human countenance; a twist that threw him into the arms of the Roman Catholic Church and accounted for sundry other dichotomies in his nature. So Lawrence notes his brusque and offhand manner, interpreting it into commonness. It was not commonness; it was a sensitive man's mask, his armour, his defence against the world. He was, without a doubt, far too fastidious in many ways, though naturally, like all persons of sound health, not inaccessible to coarser impulses at times. And thank God for that; else—whisky or no whisky—I should soon have dropped his acquaintance.

Dregs, then, was being written during the autumn of 1917 and I collaborated as best I could, and would have gone on collaborating to the end but for the fact that in October, just before the Italian defeat of Caporetto, I had to hop over the frontier. The text was different from what it now is; it contained many allusions, expunged later on, to certain ultra-masculine peculiarities of legionary life upon which I shall not expatiate here. Me they amused, these little incidents; they struck me as a natural result of local conditions; but their bestial promiscuity and utter lack of idealism horrified the fastidious Magnus more than any of his other unpleasant experiences out there; they made him sick—sick not in the American and Biblical, but in the English sense of the word: ready to vomit. Yet he put it all down with names and dates and places. Often I told him he would never get any one to print this stuff, interesting as it was from a sociological point of view; and, as a matter of fact, he showed the manuscript later in that crude state to a well-known London publisher who, after his death, remembered having seen it and wrote to me: " If you, as his literary executor, would allow the book to be expurgated, it might come out," and again nearly a year later (26th January, 1922) " How are you going to make it printable? When you have taken out the unprintable stuff there won't be a great deal left except the exciting escape from France."

Well, it has been expurgated thoroughly now —too thoroughly for my taste; a hint or two might have been left in for the guidance of the initiated. Strange, on the face of it, that Magnus should have been so averse to expunging this obnoxious material; the reason was that he had suffered so much in the Legion, and detested it so intensely, that he meant to show it up in all its crudity. ·I had to return to the attack over and over again; the last time on the very day when I left for France.

" I've given chapter and verse," he then replied, as usual. " I've just tried to tell the truth."

" You have succeeded. But truth is like that whisky of yours: not to be taken neat without disastrous consequences. You want to sell the book, don't you? No publisher would touch it with tongs as it stands. Water your truth! The reader likes to think that the legionaries, for all their roughness, are brave men ready to die for their country, and not a cosmopolitan pack of cut-throats and sharpers and sodomites."

He reflected a while and then said regretfully, as he had often said before:

" All right. I suppose I shall have to tone it down. And when I find a publisher? "

" Sell him the copyright if you can get a reasonable price for it. That will save you endless trouble."

The following May, while at St. Malo, I was surprised to receive this official letter from him :

" Rome, *May 12th*, 1918.
" Dear Norman Douglas,

" In accordance with our conversation I herewith confirm that I am willing to dispose of the copyright of *Dregs* for £150 (one hundred and fifty pounds) for America—and £150 (one hundred and fifty pounds) for Great Britain and Ireland and Colonies—in all £300 (three hundred pounds). It is understood that half the money for each country is to be paid to me at the signing of the contract and the other half to be at your entire disposal.

" Yours faithfully,
" MAURICE MAGNUS."

I wrote to ask what he meant by sending me a letter of this kind. He replied " You just keep it " or words to that effect; I therefore kept it.

It stands to reason that while writing *Dregs* he also wrote dozens of other things, as befitted that portentous American vitality of his, although the *Roman Review*, which he was editing up to that time, had unfortunately expired in consequence of the war.[1] It was characteristic of Maurice that in order to be able to work at it without distractions, he had set up its offices in the village of Monte Celio, a horrible little hill-top place near the Rome-Tivoli line where they still remember him with affection (ask the tobacconist). Monte Celio, by the way, gave him the idea for his book-plate which represents the scattered houses and old ruined castle of that place enclosed in an oval (ogival, rather) frame with the Benedictine motto : *Laborare est orare: Maurice Magnus*. This *Roman Review* was

[1] The first number of this " Weekly Review of Italian Politics, Finance, Literature, Drama, Art and Archæology," appeared on June 2nd, 1914, and the thing proceeded regularly for twenty numbers till October 14th, 1914. I cannot say whether it continued after that date.

one of several such undertakings; in Berlin, for instance, he set up a " European Literary Bureau " which seems to have done well so long as he was personally in charge of it. He wrote with great ease, but though the subjects he chose were always suggestive, his style was bald and undistinguished; and therefore, in my opinion, singularly adapted for a narrative like these Foreign Legion Memoirs, where every kind of literary artifice would have been out of place. To the very end he continued to bombard editors and agencies on both sides of the Atlantic with these things.[1] Where are they now? I possess nothing of his save " The Future Social Order of Western Civilisation " and three long chapters of what was going to be an important book entitled *Memoirs of Golden Russia.* Those I have deal with St. Petersburg, the Crimea and the " Heart of Russia "; another, on the Caucasus, which I have never seen, was also finished; others which he had in preparation described Poland, Finland, and " Three years after." I shall be glad to hand my three to any editor who cares to print them. Few foreigners knew Russia as well as he did; he spoke the language fairly well, and whenever he had occasion to write me a postcard he always spelt the English words in Russian characters.

[1] He wrote for *The Bellman* articles on the " Position of the Vatican in Relation to the War," on " Present Conditions in Italy," and " The American Spirit and Italian Propaganda." There may be more of them.

Altogether he was a far more civilised and multi-facetted person than the reader of Lawrence's Introduction might be led to expect. He made researches at the Goethe-Archiv in Weimar on several occasions. I also remember once asking him to write down for me what was worth seeing in Florence besides those monuments and galleries which the unfortunate tourist cannot help seeing. He happened to dislike Florence, but, for all that, had made it his business to do the place thoroughly, and at once sat down to indite a formidable list of convents, out-of-the-way palaces and private houses where this or that could be seen—many of which I have not heard of to this day, and hope to live long enough never to inspect.

The last things he wrote were "Vignettes of Malta": he was engaged on them at the time of his suicide. I should like to see these Vignettes; they are probably deposited in that *one old leather suit-case* above-mentioned. During this final and sad period he was straining every nerve to get out of debt; in his last letter to me—a letter which bears the Malta postmark of the 4th November, the very day of his death—he wrote: "How can one continue to live like this? I have sixty manuscripts out (including translations), at least half of them accepted, and not one paid. This is irrespective of the stuff I am doing now." Surely a pathetic state of affairs! And here I must quote a few words from p. 92 of Lawrence's Introduction, if only to show how biography ought not to be written.   Says Lawrence :

" Now would you believe it, that little scamp M—— spent over a hundred pounds of borrowed money during his four months in Malta, when his expenses, he boasted to me, need not have been more than a pound a week, once he got into the little house at Notabile.   That is, he spent at least seventy pounds too much.   Heaven knows what he did with it, apart from ' guzzling.' . . ."

The truth is that he did not spend over a hundred pounds of borrowed money; he never borrowed a hundred; apart from what he got from Lawrence, who must surely by now have recouped himself many times over by the sale of these Memoirs, he borrowed fifty-five : neither more nor less.   There lies before me an official statement of account drawn up by his Consul and entitled " Debts of the Estate of the late M. Magnus." From this document it appears that the total of his debts was £77 16s. 11¾d.; this total includes not only those fifty-five and all his outstanding trades-men's bills, but also the sum of £7 19s. 4d. which was due to the Consul for expenses in connection with Maurice's *funeral*.   As to spending seventy pounds too much, presumably on " guzzling "—he wrote me himself that the typing of his innumerable articles cost him more than did his food, which consisted for the most part of " rice and eggs, bread and tea."   I have also a letter from the gentleman whom Lawrence calls Mr. Mazzaiba, who was in daily contact with Maurice and, as his creditor for the fifty-five pounds, hardly disposed to say flattering things about him, since he never expected to get his money back. Well, this gentleman wrote me one month after the suicide (4th December, 1920) that Maurice had " lived here in a very retired and economical way." *Great is the power of misrepresentation*, as even the sweet-natured Darwin once complained. But of course the whole thing is sheer bunkum : the novelist's touch.

There reaches me at this moment a copy of the London *Spectator* of 13th December. It contains the following letter on which I shall make no comment beyond saying that it appears the writer of it had not read Lawrence's Introduction but only a review of it; that there seems to be something wrong with the last sentence, and that I hope to be forgiven for reprinting without permission.

" SIR,

" From England, six thousand miles away, the *Spectator* (always welcome) of October 18th has just arrived. In the ' Literary Suppt.' there is a commentary on M. M.'s *Memoirs of the Foreign Legion*, edited by Mr. D. H. Lawrence, headed ' The Little Gentleman Enlists.' While either I or my husband live, M. M. is not without a friend in this world to put in a good word for him; and I hope this necessarily belated word may find space in your paper. M. M. was a dear friend of mine, and, as I knew him in Italy, ' a very parfyt gentil knight '; generous, super-sensitive — not very practical. His friends I did not meet. If Mr. Lawrence is a specimen he was unfortunate in them. Cannot that superior person, so anxious to cast stones of old grudges at his unresisting dead friend, so willing to enhance his own literary reputation, and damn his friend's, by turning sarcastic phrases at his expense, imagine what a man of M. M.'s temperament suffered in those three months? He described them to me as ' Hell.' Many whose military record stands deservedly high, who may even wear decorations, did not, I'll wager, endure a tithe of the agony and humiliation which he endured; some might not have been able to.

" M. M. lived for beauty, harmony, peace. An American citizen, he never felt at home in the hustling Republic. Italy was the land of his adoption, of his heart, of his religion. He had been brought up mainly by women, to his disadvantage; and perhaps only a woman could fully understand, and so forgive, the seeming lack of courage on which we are apt to be hardest. He repudiated with passion his German blood. Long before the war, the Slav in him (Polish, I think) shuddered away from the coarseness, and what he called the lack of civilisation in the German mentality. He was writing on this very theme when the war caught

him unawares.[1] Domestic tragedy arising out of
the war led him to make the ghastly mistake of
enlisting in the Foreign Legion. No one who knew
him could imagine that he could ' stick ' that
particular ordeal, for which life had in no way
prepared him. Yet he faced it, for a quarrel not
his own, with a like chivalry that enabled him to
nurse an invalid mother for years as tenderly as
any daughter. That he failed is surely rather
matter for ' pity and terror ' than for cheap
gibes.

" If he left ' victims ' whom he had ' defrauded '
I refuse to believe he defaulted willingly. Indeed,
he wrote to us in anguish about the struggle he was
making to meet his liabilities. He thought he had
found an asylum in Malta where he could take
breath and retrieve his losses. But it seems not.
At the last, as he told an American friend, he ' could
not face an Italian prison.' Poor M. M. ' What
(he) aspired to be, and was not, comforts me.' For
him ' the high ' indeed ' proved too high '; ' the

---

[1] I have received from an unexpected quarter a mass of
literary material of his, and it has given me a melancholy
satisfaction to go through the proofs of his activities in
many departments of thought. Among these remains is
the typescript of a short but almost finished book which,
according to the Table of Contents, was to consist of twenty-
three chapters. Twenty-one of them are here written. It is
entitled " The Unspeakable Prussian—Personal Experiences
before the War—by an American Resident," and dedicated to
*all my fellow-sufferers who have come into contact with
Prussian officialdom and thereby suffered indignities and out-
rage.* This is doubtless the book above referred to.

heroic for earth too hard,' but these he was 'worth to God,' and to his sorrowing, remembering, understanding friends, one of whom I am proud to subscribe myself.

      " I am, Sir, etc.

          " IRENE M. ASHBY MACFADYEN.

" KING WILLIAM'S TOWN,
    " CAPE PROVINCE, SOUTH AFRICA."

I spoke just now of the novelist's touch in biography. What is this touch? It consists, I should say, in a failure to realise the profundities and complexities of the ordinary human mind; it selects for literary purposes two or three facets of a man or woman, generally the most spectacular and therefore " useful " ingredients of their character, and disregards all the others. Whatever fails to fit in with these specially chosen traits is eliminated; must be eliminated, for otherwise the description would not hold water. Such and such are the data; everything incompatible with those data has to go by the board. It follows that the novelist's touch argues, often logically, from a wrong premise; it takes what it likes and leaves the rest. The facts may be correct so far as they go, but there are too few of them; what the author says may be true, and yet by no means the truth. That is the novelist's touch. It falsifies life.

In Lawrence's Introduction, for example, I am

described as a blustering railer of the old school; it
would plainly never befit such a personage to feel
anything but contempt for an "effeminate little
bounder" as Magnus is described; I am therefore
made to *despise* him. I have already explained
what the truth of this matter was. Again, Magnus
most unfortunately borrowed money from Lawrence
(and the reader, by the way, will not be long in
discovering that this financial transaction imparts
a peculiarly acrid flavour to his Introduction). Now
let us try to be fair to my young friend; it is so easy
to be unfair! No doubt it hurts to part with money
to a person whom one does not care for and who
will presumably never pay it back—especially when
one has none to spare oneself; it is enough to enrage
anyone—especially friend Lawrence who (page 24)
upholds the fine middle-class tradition to "keep a
few pounds between himself and the world." Yes;
no doubt it hurts, and no doubt Maurice was a
sponger on that occasion. I should not have
taken it amiss, accordingly, if Lawrence had vented
his wrath more viciously than he does over this
particular business, since it would only prove what
a sage person said to me long ago: "There are
some people from whom it is unsafe to borrow
money." Our friend, however, is not satisfied with
voicing his personal grievance; those borrowed
pounds have caused him to give to posterity an
entirely false portrait of Magnus as a whole; he
passes from the particular to the general and so

furnishes an admirable illustration of the novelist's touch. On page 82 you will find him writing, as if he had known Magnus all his life, that he *traded on the tenderness of others;* that " God knows how much warm kindness, generosity, was showered on him during the course of his forty-odd years. And selfish little scamp, he took it as a greedy boy takes cakes off a dish, etc." [1]

Rubbish. I wish Lawrence could have met him

---

[1] Since the publication of this pamphlet a good many letters have reached me from friends of Magnus; all of them testify to his generous instincts. I will give only two extracts. An Italian gentleman, unknown to myself, writes in English from Rapallo (7th February, 1925): " . . . It is not a question of sympathy, friendship, and affection for Maurice Magnus, nor of my sorrow for his sad end. Magnus really has no need of my defence, as all who knew him thoroughly—and they are many—will not, even for a moment, believe that Mr. Lawrence can have seen a moral and spiritual side of Magnus that was unknown to them; because they know that, notwithstanding his rather nervous, snappish manner at times, he was a true *signore,* a gentleman, with a most refined taste, a love of art and literature, and a strange touch of ecclesiastic nobility, like an old-time Knight of Malta. He was an earnest, honest worker; generous, almost prodigal. . . ." And an American gentleman, unknown to myself, writes from New York (8th May, 1925) : " . . . I was acquainted with Maurice Magnus during my student days, way back in 1910 (possibly 1911, I do not quite remember). When I first read Mr. Lawrence's lengthy Introduction to *The Memoirs of the Foreign Legion,* it never occurred to me that " M. M." was that splendid young gentleman whose pleasurable and interesting acquaintance I enjoyed for about a year; and many a pleasant evening I enjoyed in his two wonderfully appointed rooms in Gramercy Park. During the ten months or so that I had the pleasure of his acquaintance I learned that I was in the company of a gentleman not of the ordinary type; always solicitous for the comfort and welfare of others; always giving rather than accepting."

during one of his many rich moments; he would have had another tale to unfold. And I wish the Recording Angel could be induced to flutter down for five minutes or so and open that note-book of his and tell us exactly how often Maurice sponged on his friends, and how often they sponged on him. . . .

Poor biographers, these romance-writers; and poor psychologists. That is because they work on the *Leitmotif* system, which gives fallacious results when applied to a delicate structure like the human mind. A little intuition would have convinced anybody but a novelist-creditor that Magnus was too generous for this world; that his giving capacities far surpassed his borrowing ones; that if he was sometimes without means it was only because he had spent them on friends and strangers and not on himself, as a relatively poor man ought to have done; that he was one of those people who are never happy, never quite happy, unless they are obliging others—for which, of course, they get the devil's thanks. Thomas à Kempis, or some other neurotic, had given him a firm belief in the comfortable but preposterous fiction of the perfectibility of mankind; he therefore went out of his way, over and over again, to return good for evil and, do what I would, I never succeeded in causing him to excrete this particular virus. Now I will not go so far as to say that a certain proportion of our fellow-creatures may not be amenable to such kind treatment; but their numbers are so inconsiderable, so lamentably small that I, for my part, have long ceased looking for them. Not so Magnus. He looked for them. He was determined to do good whenever possible.

There is in Florence a certain tavern known as the " Café delle C——e " which at night-time becomes, or became, a sinister place—the haunt of pimps and every other kind of *louche* and dubious character. Thither we used to resort after dinner, to study types; and one evening, I remember, Maurice was attracted by an ancient man at the other end of the room, poorly dressed and sipping his coffee with trembling hands. He could not take his eyes off him.

" You see him? " he asked. " Looks as if he had been through Hell, doesn't he? And at least seventy years old, I should say. He won't last much longer. Poor old boy, I'll bet he only came in here for the sake of the warmth."

" Very likely."

After a while he began again :

" I just can't stand that unhappy face. I'm going to give him every cent I have in this pocket; it's only eight or nine francs—" and he got up from the table. I pulled him back.

" Not in here," I said. " We shall be taken for millionaires and waylaid on the road before we get home. You must do it outside."

There we waited. Our coffee-drinker never moved; he was enjoying the warmth. And time went by. I grew sleepy and grumpy, yearning to go to bed, and did my best to make Maurice change his mind. He refused to budge. At last, after about two hours, the place was closed and we were all driven out including our man, who went off in a direction different from our own. We followed him for twenty paces or so and then Maurice, with a single word " Permettete," slipped the money into his hand and turned back before the old fellow had time to recover from his surprise. How many of my readers would have acted thus? Would friend Lawrence have done so? And this is the man of whom he writes that he had " no bowels of deep compassion or kindliness."

In this case the money may have been well spent; in others he certainly erred on the side of generosity. We knew a vile creature in Rome whom Magnus one day insisted upon inviting to luncheon, for no reason whatever. Why not, he said?

" That slimy abortion? " I asked. " Don't invite him to luncheon. Stamp on him."

" Ah," he said, " but one must be kind to these people. If you only knew what he's been through—"

" And richly deserved it; with that face of his. Stamp on him. He'll do you a bad turn whenever he gets a chance."

Prophetic utterance. . . . It was precisely this reptile who through the indiscreet confidences of a friend was enabled to put the Italian police on his tracks, first at the monastery mentioned by Lawrence, and then in Malta; and so led to his suicide. It is to be hoped that somebody has stamped on him by this time. He ought to be pounded into such a jelly that his own mother would have difficulty in recognising the remains.

Now what, one may ask—what made the loathsome creature act as he did? Nothing but malice; natural malice; an excess of biliary secretion indirectly due, I fancy, to that pestilential system of repression which of late has invaded every department of life. I can find no other explanation for the deplorable fact that so many people seem nowadays to live in a chronic state of envy, hatred, malice, and all uncharitableness. Be my theory of its origin correct or not, this exacerbation is indubitably a recent phenomenon; and not an attractive one. " The modern temper," writes a lady, " cannot respect, cannot appreciate, cannot love (cannot laugh, she might have added), *but it can hate.*" True! And how hateful is this hate!

It is astonishing that Lawrence never noticed this streak of unworldliness in Magnus; it would be astonishing, that is, but for the fact that he happens to belong to that literary class which refuses to see more than two or three aspects of their fellow-creatures. He had made up his mind that Maurice was to be classed as a sponger; the quality of unworldliness being inconsistent with such a character must therefore be wiped out of the portrait. And out it goes. . . .

What children, what innocents are these writing gentlemen beside the family doctor or solicitor who lack their petty pictorial sense and the obligation to tickle a certain class of fool-readers; who make it their business to see mankind as a whole and therefore possess more psychology and penetration in their little finger than your average novelist in his whole inflated organism! Go to those others for amusement if you like, and if you think you can find it there; not for knowledge of human nature.

I have heard the late Joseph Conrad called a great psychologist, and that is a good example for my purpose. Well, Conrad was first and foremost a Pole and, like many Poles, a politician and a moralist *malgré lui*. These are his fundamentals. He was also a great writer with hardly an ounce of psychology in his composition. His genius is the reverse of the psychologist's; it consists in driving you along by main force; in making characters work out their salvation according to the approved principles not of psychology but of British morality, of the " right thing to do." Such was his implicit teaching: the " right thing to do." Everything that deviated from this precarious standard was anathema to him; so much anathema that even the harmless failing of his friend Stephen Crane is politely slurred over. He seldom explored the

human heart, that wonderful tangle of motives pure
and impure (as they are called)—which was a pity,
for he might have picked up some humour as he
went along; he never so much as glanced into its
depths lest he should discover, down in those muddy
recesses, something rotten, something which had no
right to be there. Can a man who lacks sympathy
with erring humanity give us a convincing picture of
it? He can give us no more than what Conrad
gave: a convincing proof of how much may be
accomplished without psychology.

And if this be true of an imposing figure like
his, how about the smaller fry? I pick up an
ordinary novel now and then, and ask myself
whether we shall go on reading this flatulent balder-
dash much longer. I hope not. For what is the
ordinary novel but a string of foregone conclusions;
a barrel-organ wound up to play one particular
tune? Any hall porter, any genuine *homo sapiens*
with all his little caprices and contradictions,
blundering by chance into the entrails of this pitiful
mechanism, forthwith puts the whole machine out
of order. Life would indeed be a bore, if constructed on the lines of the ordinary novel. And
biography, the record of life, would become a
despicable farce if enlivened or rather infected, as
in this case, with that pernicious novelist's touch
which menaces the living, wrongs the dead, and
degrades a decent literary calling to the level of the
chatter at an old maids' tea-party.

It menaces the living. It adds a new terror to life; to the lives, at least, of those who are not blest with the hide of a rhinoceros. Here is friend Lawrence, in an earlier book, dragging me in again together with a number of my friends—and really, are we as interesting as all that? Can modern writers describe only people they know? Are they too lazy or too stupid to create a character of their own?—me, under the transparent disguise of Jimmie McTaggart or something equally Scotch (I have not the book here) with the same *Leitmotif* as in this Introduction but not so cleverly done; the same high-handed old swaggerer, rather unsteady on his legs, and giving utterance to opinions which are quite in harmony with this romantic figure but which, as a matter of fact, have never yet entered my head. And here I must delay a moment, to draw attention to what seems an urgent question of literary etiquette. If Lawrence had caused me to discuss William Shakespeare or Mr. Gladstone he might have let me say what he pleased; my imaginary views on these subjects, however fantastic, could have done no possible harm to anybody. But he has pictured me as commenting on certain living personal friends of mine who also appear in the book, and has put into my mouth some uncomplimentary and spiteful observations about them which—consistent as they may be with his portrait of me—I never dreamt of uttering and which, as he cannot but have foreseen, have given a little pain to the persons concerned. Is this fair? I think not. I call it something more than the novelist's touch; it is hitting below the belt, and a damnably vulgar proceeding. There was no reason why he should annoy people who, while he was in the place, fed him to bursting-point and went out of their way to show him every civility in their power. Such, alas, is friend Lawrence who is fond of introducing familiars in this playful fashion (with results which are sometimes pecuniarily disastrous to himself) and whose behaviour, for the rest, is symptomatic; he has only caught the tone of the times, seeing that an entire school has grown up which lives, and thrives, on writing up other people in books and newspapers.

Now this personality-mongering is a nuisance which has increased, is increasing, and ought to be diminished. It is not only bad literature but bad breeding. You can hardly pick up any volume by a member of this school without finding therein caricatures of some acquaintance—all unfavourably drawn and derided not with frank wit or invective or mockery or Rabelaisian laughter, but with that squeaky suburban chuckle which is characteristic of an age of eunuchs. And if they are momentarily at a loss for friends to distort, they indulge in airing their own private sensations—a mild form of exhibitionism—with a shamelessness that reminds one of nothing so much as a female dog. Questionable taste! It seems to me that even such a writing man should have some manners, some reserve, though his mentality be of the non-human order and his ethos immeasurably inferior to that of the butcher or grocer; that if he cannot respect his neighbours, he ought at least to respect himself. But he has forgotten what self-respect means; everything is grist to his mill—including himself, and it is no use appealing to his better nature, since he has no nature at all.

The ridiculous compilation known as *Who's Who* has done a good deal towards fostering this unhealthy interest in the affairs of other people. That Sir Edmund Gosse happens to write good books is no reason why the public should be informed how much he pays his scullery-maid; and what on earth does it matter to anyone, save himself and his friends, what his favourite indoor amusements are—whether he prefers bridge to baccarat, or ping-pong to dominoes? Vastly offensive, this prying and rapacious meddlesomeness. But I fear we shall never have a revulsion of feeling against such snobbishly genteel hankerings. They are part of that universal levelling-down process for which the education-of-people-who-ought-never-to-be-educated is responsible.

I received not long ago a copy of a well-known Jewish monthly from America wherein, to my surprise, I discovered an " Imaginary Conversation " between myself and the author, a young

R

Jewish friend of mine, on the subject of " Judaism and Paganism " : he supporting the Jewish point of view and I the other. Now it strikes me that a man who has written " Far be it from me to disparage the tribe of Israel. I have gained the conviction—firm-fixed, now, as the Polar Star—that the Hebrew is as good a man as the Christian—" it strikes me that such a man can hardly be put forward as a representative Jew-baiter. Could he not have found somebody more qualified for the post; Mr. Belloc, for instance? He might with some plausibility have introduced me as anti-Christian. . . . But I shall not wrangle over the religious aspects of the matter; they are not worth wrangling about, since Christians are only an anæmic variety of Jews. It is the principle involved which concerns me. There ought to be a limit to this kind of thing; the limit being that a writer, before displaying you in a wholly fictitious character and putting into your mouth arguments which, whether sound or not, have never yet occurred to you, should at least be good enough to ask your permission first. Only a little fun, of course. My young friend meant no harm; he probably thought that in proclaiming me across the length and breadth of a continent as an anti-Semite and himself as a Semite he was *giving the old dodderer a lift-up*—and himself another one. Well, we may all be vainer than we think and still ready to dispense with this form of advertisement. Not that I am annoyed personally, having long ago convinced myself of the truth of the saying that no man was ever written down except by himself, but there is this to be considered: like others, I have excellent Jewish friends over there; Jews are more sensitive than they look, and one or the other of them, if he comes across this article, may think that it throws a new light on my sentiments towards his race, and be justifiably sore about it. No matter. *Il faut avaler son crapaud*, as Zola used to say.

This was just a friendly joke; it is otherwise with many of the things I have lately read which verge, and often trespass, on the libellous—if one could bring oneself to take their authors at their own valuation. Certainly it is an anomalous state of affairs that respectable folk should be at the mercy of a band of dirt-throwers who are coining money at their expense; it suggests that in such matters of literary ethics we might do worse than return to the more gentlemanlike standard of the Victorians, though we shall obviously never have real manners, either in literature or in society, until duelling becomes popular again. Duelling would soon put an end to these caddish arts and to several other inconveniences as well; there would be no more low-class allusions to living people in novels or newspapers or memoirs if their authors realised that by next morning they might have half a yard of cold steel in their gizzards.

Meanwhile it is not an exhilarating spectacle:

this confraternity of cats—among whom many people, I fear, will include friend Lawrence, if not on account of this performance, then on account of others—industriously scribbling down, with more or less untruthfulness, the imperfections of their fellow-creatures; and the literary historian of the future, dipping into these outpourings and casting about for a word that shall summarise the flabby activities of the whole tribe, may well find himself at fault.　I think he will end in calling it the school of cerebral hermaphrodites.　Sexlessness is its basic note.　How one yearns for a Pope to laugh their monkey-tricks out of existence, or for a Byron to disembowel these epicene babblers and wipe the floor with what is left of them!　Byron, needless to say, is out of fashion in those virginal circles.　He happened to be a man. . . .

Maybe friend Lawrence, should he read what has gone before, will think it is pointed straight at himself, whereas he is only the *causa causans*. That cannot be helped.　He has undoubtedly made a spleenful hash of Maurice Magnus, but we can none of us transcend the boundaries of our own natures; he is an impulsive, elvish mortal who writes whatever comes into his head, and hates being pestered for money by bounders.　Once we have grasped these initial facts, we know our position; we are prepared for the worst.

We get it.　On p. 85, for instance, he achieves

as fine a specimen of malicious rhetoric as you may
come across in a week of Sundays; mere rant, in
fact, when one considers the circumstances which
were just these: Maurice Magnus, like others,
caught the war-fever. After applying vainly for all
kinds of jobs (see p. 101; and these applications
were authentic, for I have read them and the replies
to them) he committed the nightmarish blunder of
enlisting in the Foreign Legion where a natural
refinement in habits and manners and language
intensified his sufferings a thousandfold. What he
thought of this Legion is set down in the few
temperate pages constituting Chapters 6 and 17
which bear the hall-mark of veracity, and which I
warmly commend to my readers together with the
words, so full of restraint, at the bottom of p. 240:
" For I knew there was a limit to how long I could
keep sane, etc." And as if one could expect a
German-American-Jew or, for that matter, any other
sensible person, to feel strongly on the subject
of nationality! One may dislike individuals; to
dislike an entire nation is a feat of which only fools
are capable. Now Maurice, whatever his failings,
was no fool. He wrote me himself: " I agree with
Tim Edwards that some people have no nationality. I am sure I have not." Though his opinion
of German culture was fairly pronounced (see
p. 245) he was no more anti-German than anti-
Chinese; he detested oppression in every shape or
form. That is why he loathed German brutality

and insolence; why he sympathised with French soldiers huddled together like cattle in a train; why it made his "blood boil" to see how poor Arabs were treated by the officials. . . .

Such was Maurice who could not bear cruel dealing between man and man, and was therefore not long in discovering that the Foreign Legion did not suit his temperament. To escape out of that Hell was an undertaking full of danger; one single false step would have been his ruin; it called for a rare alloy of cunning and grit—grit of an uncommon kind. Finally, after mature preparation, he burnt all his papers and walked out of the trap as unconcernedly as Napoleon walked out of the fortress of Ham; with this difference, that the consequences of re-capture would have certainly been more serious for Maurice. He strolled into Italy, and was safe.

On a later occasion, but still in troubled times, he strolled into France again.

One morning at Mentone, just as I was finishing my breakfast, he turned up unexpectedly, more spick and span than ever, informed me that he had no passport or papers of any kind, but, having just received a biggish cheque, could not resist the temptation of trying his luck at Monte Carlo again after all those years. Knowing how conscientiously the frontier was guarded, I asked how he had done the trick and how he now proposed to manage at

Mentone with that pathologically suspicious *commissaire de police*, whom I knew only too well.

He had stayed a day or two at Ventimiglia, he explained; made friends with a fisherman and finally induced him to row him over at dead of night and deposit him with his bag on the Mentone beach. There he had waited under a boulder till dawn came, then gone as usual to the most expensive hotel and enjoyed a bath, shave, change of apparel and breakfast. He must, he simply must, have a flutter at the tables—just a little one. And as he could not stay three hours at an hotel without producing a *carte d'identité*, would I persuade my landlord to give him a room somewhere near my quarters? I did; but it cost some trouble.

Luck was against him at the Casino.

"Never mind," he said. "I know the whole history of Monaco and Monte Carlo. I'll write an article about the place to recoup myself. I've bought the photographs already."

He wrote that article (I typing it) in one day and sent it to some monthly in the Middle West; with what results I cannot tell. But this ought to be noted: a man who can write three articles a week and have two or even one of them accepted is not making a bad income. It was different, however, during that particular period when nobody wanted such literature, and this accounts to a large extent for the difficulties in which he latterly found himself.

Meanwhile my landlord had grown so restive about this possible spy in his house that Maurice decided Mentone was no longer the place for him. He wrote to his fisherman at Ventimiglia.

" I've told him," he said, " to fetch me next Tuesday on the esplanade at half-past one in the morning. He's sure to turn up! But we must be sitting there a good deal earlier, so as not to attract attention."

We were on our bench by midnight. It was pitch-dark and rather windy, and I thought that for once he had miscalculated his man, for at 1.15 no boat was yet in sight. Suddenly it appeared with four oarsmen moving not along the shore but from straight out at sea; he jumped on board before it touched land; I threw his bag after him; the operation took half a minute.

" Hi! Your cane! " I called out. I found I was still holding it in my hand, to allow him to jump in more easily.

" Damn my cane! "

They were already out of reach.

This little trip to Mentone, I should imagine, was an epitome of Maurice's whole life.

Finally he went over to Malta and worked like a nigger to straighten out his affairs again. While so doing, that foul creature in Rome whom I have mentioned set the Italian police on his tracks with a view to having him extradited for a certain debt incurred in Italy. If only he had told me the complete truth! But he was always shy about disclosing his troubles to me; he had a strange reluctance to give me any kind of pain or even preoccupation. I knew he was hard up; had I known of this particular Italian embarrassment, I should have recommended him to go not to Malta but to Corfu, where he could have worked to his heart's content without fear of being interrupted by bailiffs and detectives. So useful it is to know a smattering of the laws of the countries you inhabit; so much more useful than knowing their languages. . . .

Anyhow, they pounced on him at Malta, and, in a moment of supreme weakness, he killed himself rather than fall into their hands. That he was able to face the horrors of life among the unspeakable riff-raff of the Legion, and yet unable to face the slight inconvenience of appearing in an Italian court on a charge of fraud and perhaps doing a month or two, is to me an almost inexplicable phenomenon. I suppose he had a queer sense of honour packed away somewhere, whatever his enemies may say. And, besides that, he must have been utterly run down in stamina and health; else where was his grit gone? I am not in the habit of making debts; I lack the resourceful vitality necessary for evading creditors, and prefer to spend what energies I have in the pursuit of other objects; but had I been in Maurice's place on that occasion,

I should have acted differently. Fancy poisoning yourself because you owe a little money to a brigand —a notorious brigand, too—of a continental hotel-keeper! Maurice ought to have faced the music, and then blackmailed him for the rest of his life.

Previously to this, however, he had borrowed fifty-five pounds from his Maltese friend Mr. Mazzaiba, and this financial transaction gives Lawrence an opportunity for a grand pyrotechnical display of sympathy for the poor deluded victim, Mr. Mazzaiba. Poor Mr. Mazzaiba! Now why is Lawrence so terribly vexed because a certain bounder owes money to a third party and has the impudence to kill himself before paying it back? There is more than meets the eye here. A little overdone, this pity for Mr. Mazzaiba; it does not ring quite true. Is it perhaps a vicarious, unconfessed pity for himself? That is probably where the shoe pinches. Not that I would be construed as saying he is guilty of deliberate simulation here; so far as I have observed, he never simulates; his method is to work himself up to a state of wrong feeling and then let fly in a needlessly shrill tone of voice. This whole Introduction is an example of the process. It is wrong feeling nearly all the way through; wrongly bitter; a touch of Maurice's humanity would do our friend no harm —which reminds me that the writer of the *Outlook* article, from whom I quoted at the beginning, seems to have made a mistake when he says he is assured that Lawrence has " contrived to exalt himself at the expense of the dead Maurice Magnus." At least, that is not how I should put it. I think a careful study of this Introduction will convince most readers that my young friend has not exalted himself to any great extent; that on the contrary, in exposing the frailties of Maurice Magnus he has contrived, like a true Boswell, to expose his own.

Be that as it may, it is worth noting that Mr. Mazzaiba himself, the long-suffering creditor for those fifty-five pounds, must have taken another and most singular view of this " Judas treachery," as Lawrence calls it. Despite his grievance against Maurice, he went to the expense of having his remains moved from the public grave at Malta and interred in his own burial-place; which says a good deal for both of them, and proves, among other things, that some people can still be trusted to behave like gentlemen.

And there he now lies, the poor devil; unconcerned about bailiffs—and biographers. *Requiescat.* Lawrence calls him an outsider: it is the mildest of some fifteen pretty names he bestows on him. An outsider. So be it. I wish we had a few more such outsiders on earth.

[SYRACUSE
        24th December, 1924]

Date Due

DE 4 '69			
	PRINTED IN U. S. A.		